Lesson Assessment Book 1

Annotated Teacher's Edition

Level 3

McGraw Hill **SRA**

A Division of The **McGraw-Hill** Companies

SRAonline.com

 SRA

Send all inquiries to this address:
SRA/McGraw-Hill
4400 Easton Commons
Columbus, OH 43219-6188

ISBN: 978-0-07-613090-0
MHID: 0-07-613090-8

2 3 4 5 6 7 8 9 MAZ 13 12 11 10 09 08

The *McGraw-Hill* Companies

Table of Contents

Imagine It! Lesson Assessment Books

Lesson Assessment Book 1 and *Lesson Assessment Book 2* are an integral part of a complete assessment program that aligns with the instruction in *Imagine It! Lesson Assessment Book 1* covers material from Units 1–3. *Lesson Assessment Book 2* covers material from Units 4–6. The skills featured in lesson assessments are tied to reading success and reflect both state and national standards.

Lesson Assessment Book 1 and *Lesson Assessment Book 2* offer the opportunity for summative and formative assessment. As students complete each lesson, they will be assessed on their understanding of the instructional content and the literature in each lesson. The results of the assessments will then be used to inform subsequent instruction. How students score on the assessments offers a picture of current student achievement status while also guiding you toward appropriate instructional decisions.

Each lesson assessment offers you the ability to gauge students' understanding of and growth in the following areas:

• Vocabulary
• Comprehension
• Grammar, Usage, and Mechanics
• Oral Fluency
• Writing

Lesson Assessments

The lesson assessments consist of the following:

Lesson Area	Format	Scope	Scoring
Vocabulary	Multiple Choice	Selection Vocabulary and Word Structure elements	10 points (5 questions x 2 point)
Comprehension	Multiple Choice	Comprehension Skills	5 points (5 questions x 1 point)
	Short Answer	Comprehension Skills	10 points (5 questions x 2 points)
	Linking to the Concepts (Short Answer)	General comprehension related to a selection	4 points (0-4 rubrics)
	Personal Response (Short Answer)	General comprehension related to a selection	3 points (0-3 rubrics)
	Analyzing the Selection (Extended Response)	Understanding and development of ideas about selections and the unit theme	8 points (0-8 rubrics)
Grammar, Usage, and Mechanics	Multiple Choice	Grammar, Usage, and Mechanics skills practiced in the lesson	10 points (5 questions x 2 point)
Oral Fluency	Teacher-Directed Student Performance	Oral fluency development from lesson to lesson	Accuracy Rate on 100-point scale

Students will be graded on their understanding of the vocabulary, word structure, comprehension, and grammar, usage, and mechanics skills taught in the lesson on a 50-point scale. A score of 80% (or 40 points out of 50) or higher on each lesson assessment is expected. Students may look back at the selection to answer the assessment questions. Students who consistently fall below 80% should be monitored for possible intervention. Students who are consistent low-performers in one or more aspects of the lesson assessment should be offered more practice in this lesson area during Workshop.

The Oral Fluency Assessments are scored separately. These assessments offer further data on student abilities. Student performance on oral fluency assessments is often a reliable predictor of student growth and understanding in other lesson areas. Students with consistently low accuracy rates and below-level words per minute numbers should be provided extra fluency practice during Workshop.

End of Unit Writing Prompt

Over the course of the year, students will encounter six writing prompts, two each in the narrative, expository, and persuasive genres. These prompts reflect students' prior knowledge and experience with writing to a specific genre. Each prompt consists of a writing situation, a specific audience, directions for writing, and a checklist students can reference to ensure they receive the best score possible. Rubrics for scoring student work follow each prompt in this book. These rubrics pertain to genre, writing traits, and conventions. Students will be graded on a 20-point scale based on the rubrics—four points multiplied by five key writing features.

A score of 75% (or 15 points out of 20) or higher on each writing prompt is expected. Students can respond to the prompts in their student workbooks.

Scores and Records

The opening page of each lesson assessment includes a place for students to write their names and the date, and for you to list their scores.

The Oral Fluency Assessment includes a box in which to write the accuracy rate.

The writing prompt includes a place for students to write their names and the date, and for you to list their scores.

Students' scores in the assessment can be registered in the Oral Fluency Scores, Class Assessment Record, and Student Assessment Record pages.

Lesson Assessment Sections

Students may look back at the selection to answer the assessment questions.

Vocabulary

Each vocabulary assessment is comprised of five multiple-choice questions worth two points each. Four of the questions feature selection vocabulary words from the lesson students have just completed. The remaining question in the assessment pertains to a word structure element from that lesson. The format of this question varies based on the word structure feature that is being assessed.

Comprehension: Multiple Choice

Each comprehension assessment begins with five multiple-choice questions worth one point each. The items reflect the comprehension skills students have been taught specifically in that lesson and skills students have been previously taught.

Comprehension: Short Answer

Next, students answer five short-answer questions worth two points each. These questions also reflect comprehension skills specific to the lesson and to students' prior knowledge and understanding of comprehension skills. Well-crafted and concise responses that answer the question fully should be awarded two points. Answers that partially address the question or are confusing and incomplete should be awarded a point, at your discretion. Answers that do not attempt to address the question or provide incorrect information should receive zero points.

Please note the "Possible answers below" following the directions in this Teacher's Edition. This serves as a reminder that students do not have to provide the exact answer shown, and that in some cases more than one answer is possible. For example, questions that ask for "one reason" or "one example" of something might be answered by a reason or example not specified in this Teacher's Edition.

Comprehension: Linking to the Concepts

In this section, students craft a response to a question related to the selection they have just read. These questions do not focus on a particular comprehension skill; rather, they assess general comprehension of a selection by focusing on a key element in a selection which students should be comfortable identifying and writing to or about. These questions are worth four points each. Use the following criteria to judge student responses. To fully answer the question or prompt, student answers should be approximately thirty to sixty words.

Score: 4

The student understands the question and responds using information from the selection. The response is correct, reflects a thorough comprehension of the selection, and is an acceptably complete answer to the question. The organization of the response is meaningful, it is written smoothly, and sentences flow together. The response focuses on the topic. If multiple paragraphs are written, they are linked to one another with effective transitions. The response reads easily and demonstrates a sense of audience. It has correct spelling, grammar, usage, and mechanics, and it is written neatly and legibly.

Score: 3

The student understands the question and responds using information from the selection. The response may reflect comprehension of the selection and is a somewhat complete answer to the question. The organization of the response is meaningful, it is written smoothly, and sentences flow together. The response focuses on the topic. If multiple paragraphs are written, they are linked to one another with effective transitions. The response reads easily and demonstrates a sense of audience. It has occasional errors in spelling, grammar, usage, and mechanics, and it is mostly written neatly and legibly.

Score: 2

The student has partial understanding of the question. The response may reflect limited comprehension of the selection and is an incomplete answer to the question. The organization of the response is weak, it is written carelessly, and sentences are somewhat disorganized. The response includes extraneous information. If multiple paragraphs are written, they are linked to one another ineffectively. The response requires some effort to read easily and demonstrates a poor sense of audience. It has occasional errors in spelling, grammar, usage, and mechanics, and it is written somewhat neatly and legibly.

Score: 1

The student has minimal understanding of the question. The response may reflect poor comprehension of the selection and is a barely acceptable answer to the question. The organization of the response is imprecise, it is written erratically, and sentences may be disjointed. The response is poorly focused. If multiple paragraphs are written, they are linked to one another inconsistently. The response is difficult to follow and may cause the reader to struggle. It has frequent errors in spelling, grammar, usage, and mechanics, and it is written with borderline neatness and legibility.

Score: 0

The student fails to compose a response. If a response is attempted, it is inaccurate, meaningless, or irrelevant. The response may be written so poorly that it is neither legible nor understandable.

The following is an example of a response that would receive a score of "4" if it were written neatly and legibly. The student shows an understanding of the question and relates information pertaining to the selection. The answer is organized, and the sections of the response relate to one another. There are no errors in spelling, grammar, usage, and mechanics. This is an exemplary response.

SAMPLE

Linking to the Concepts *How do you think Rosie felt when she saw her old family at the graduation?*

Rosie was probably happy, but she didn't show it. She didn't do anything because she was trained well. She probably wanted to jump around and lick them, but she didn't. She needed to be by her new person.

Comprehension: Personal Response

In this section, students are asked to craft a personal response related to an idea or thematic issue raised by the selection they have just read. This section judges students' level of comprehension by assessing their ability to connect what they have just read to a personal level.

These questions are worth three points each. Use the following criteria to judge student responses. To fully answer the question or prompt, student answers should be approximately thirty to sixty words.

Score: 3

The student understands the question and responds suitably using a personal experience, opinion, prior knowledge, or plausible conjecture. The response reflects a thorough comprehension of the selection and is an acceptably complete answer to the question. The organization of the response is meaningful, it is written smoothly, and sentences flow together. The response focuses on the topic. If multiple paragraphs are written, they are linked to one another with effective transitions. The response reads easily and demonstrates a sense of audience. It has correct spelling, grammar, usage, and mechanics, and it is written neatly and legibly.

Score: 2

The student understands the question and responds using a personal experience, opinion, prior knowledge, or plausible conjecture. The response may reflect partial comprehension of the selection and is a somewhat complete answer to the question. The organization of the response is imprecise, it is written erratically, and sentences may be somewhat disjointed. The response is not clearly focused. If multiple paragraphs are written, they are linked to one another ineffectively. The response is difficult to follow and demonstrates little awareness of the reader. It has a moderate number of errors in spelling, grammar, usage, and mechanics, and it is mostly written neatly and legibly.

Score: 1

The student has minimal understanding of the question and responds using a personal experience, opinion, prior knowledge, or plausible conjecture. The response may reflect poor comprehension of the selection and is a barely acceptable answer to the question. The organization of the response is imprecise, it is written erratically, and sentences may be disjointed. The response is poorly focused. If multiple paragraphs are written, they are linked to one another inconsistently. The response is difficult to follow and may cause the reader to struggle. It has frequent errors in spelling, grammar, usage, and mechanics, and it is written with borderline neatness and legibility.

Score: 0

The student fails to compose a response. If a response is attempted, it is inaccurate, meaningless, or irrelevant. The response may be written so poorly that it is neither legible nor understandable.

The following is an example of a response that would receive a score of "1" if it were written with borderline neatness and legibility. The student shows some understanding of the question. However, the response begins and ends abruptly, the reader has to guess the type of store, there is little explanation of what would be done to get people to come to the store, and there are errors in spelling and grammar.

SAMPLE

Personal Response *What kind of business would you like to open? How would you get people to come to your business?*

It would be a nice store with lots of things. People would come because the cloths would be nice and from teams like pros and colleges. It would things that girls would like and boys.

Grammar, Usage, and Mechanics

Each grammar, usage, and mechanics assessment is comprised of five multiple-choice questions worth two points each. Each question specifically relates to the lesson material for that week. Students sometimes will be asked to identify errors or incorrect constructions, so remind students to read each question carefully.

Comprehension: Analyzing the Selection

This section of the assessment allows students to craft a longer, more detailed response to show their comprehension of what they have read. It also provides additional data on the writing skills of students as they progress through the program.

Students will sometimes be asked to respond by connecting the selection they have just read to previous selections in the unit.

These questions and prompts are worth eight points each. Use the following criteria to judge student responses. To fully answer the question or prompt, student answers should be approximately ninety to one hundred and thirty words.

Note: You will notice that the rubrics below each have a two-point range. Use your professional judgment in awarding the higher point total in the scale to students' work.

Score: 8 or 7

The student understands the question and responds suitably using the appropriate source of information. These sources include the selection itself, other selections, personal experience, opinion, prior knowledge, or plausible conjecture. The response reflects a thorough comprehension of the selection and is an acceptably complete answer to the question. The organization of the response is meaningful, it is written smoothly, and both sentences and paragraphs flow together. Paragraphs focus on related topics and are linked to one another with effective transitions. The response reads easily and demonstrates a sense of audience. It has correct spelling, grammar, usage, and mechanics, and it is written neatly and legibly.

Score: 6 or 5

The student understands the question and responds suitably using the appropriate source of information. These sources include the selection itself, other selections, personal experience, opinion, prior knowledge, or plausible conjecture. The response may reflect comprehension of the selection or other sources and is a somewhat complete answer to the question. The organization of the response is somewhat meaningful, and both sentences and paragraphs flow together relatively smoothly. Paragraphs focus on related topics and are linked to one another with effective transitions. The response reads easily and demonstrates a sense of audience. It has occasional errors in spelling, grammar, usage, and mechanics, and it is written somewhat neatly and legibly.

Score: 4 or 3

The student has partial understanding of the question. The response may reflect limited comprehension of the selection and is an incomplete answer to the question or includes irrelevant information. The organization of the response is weak, it is written carelessly, and both sentences and paragraphs are somewhat disorganized. Paragraphs include some extraneous information and are linked to one another ineffectively. The response requires some effort to read easily and demonstrates a poor sense of audience. It has occasional errors in spelling, grammar, usage, and mechanics, and it is written somewhat neatly and legibly.

Score: 2 or 1

The student has minimal understanding of the question. The response may reflect poor comprehension of the selection and is a barely acceptable answer to the question or includes irrelevant information. The organization of the response is imprecise, it is written erratically, and sentences or paragraphs may be disjointed. Paragraphs may be poorly focused or are linked to one another inconsistently. The response is difficult to follow and may cause the reader to struggle. It has frequent errors in spelling, grammar, usage, and mechanics, and it is written with borderline neatness and legibility.

Score: 0

The student fails to compose a response. If a response is attempted, it is inaccurate, meaningless, or irrelevant. The response may be written so poorly that it is neither legible nor understandable.

The following is an example of a response that would receive a score of "2" if written with borderline neatness and legibility. The student does show an understanding of the question. However, the response is written erratically and has few real details and little support. There are many errors in spelling, grammar, usage, and mechanics.

SAMPLE

Analyzing the Selection   There are different kinds of selections in this unit. What are some of the things you enjoyed about each selection?

The Tomás story was good because the library lade was nice to Tomás. Liberians are pretty nice, so the story was kind of true.

Big Wind wasn't very good. I didn't like it alot. The storm store was good because they had fun even though the electricity was off. The cat was good even though it was afraid.

The pottery story was okay. It was neat how the old people taught the children about making pots. I didn't think the story was real, but we talked about it in class and some people live like that even today.

The Johnny Appleseed story I knew from before. My uncle told me about it. I think the story is true that there was a real Jonny Appleseed. There are apple trees all over so. somebody had to plant them

Oral Fluency Assessments

Administering Oral Fluency Assessments

The Oral Fluency Assessment is an efficient means for evaluating students' ability to read. It is simple to administer and score, yet it provides extraordinarily useful quantitative and qualitative data. You will find oral fluency assessments for each lesson. The words in the selections are of sufficient variety to allow for an analysis of the decoding and vocabulary abilities of a student and to draw inferences about a student's ability to derive meaning from the text.

Make a copy of the Oral Fluency Assessment for each student you will be assessing. Have students turn to the corresponding page in their workbooks. Be sure you have a pen or pencil, a stopwatch or other timer, and extra paper to record any observations. Briefly review the text before you begin. On the Oral Fluency Scores pages, you will record the student's name, the date of the assessment, and the results of the assessment.

Have the student sit comfortably at a table with you. Seat yourself and the student so that you can mark the assessment unobtrusively without distracting the student.

Say: *Here is a selection I would like you to read aloud for me. I am going to listen to you read and take some notes. The notes I take will help me learn how well you can read. You will not be graded for this, so you should not feel nervous. Read the selection carefully and do your best. Take a few minutes now to look over the selection, and then I will tell you when to begin.*

Allow time for the student to preview the story. Be sure you have a pen or pencil.

Say: *Are you ready?* (Check to be sure the student is ready.) *You may begin now.*

Start the timer or watch as the student begins to read. You may pronounce any proper nouns with which the student is unfamiliar. Do not count these words as errors.

Note: If the student becomes frustrated or makes several consecutive errors, stop the assessment.

At the end of one minute place a bracket ( ]) at the end of the last word the student reads.

Scoring Oral Fluency Assessments

The following guidelines will help you score the assessment accurately and consistently.

- Self-correcting should not be counted as an error.
- Repeating the same mistake should be counted as only one error.
- Hesitating for more than five seconds—at which point you would have provided the word—should count as an error.
- Become familiar with the evaluating codes before administering the Oral Fluency Assessment.

Scoring Conventions

- Draw a line through any word that is misread. Count this as an error. If possible, note the type of error. (Misreading *short a* as *short e*, reading *get* as *jet*, and so on).
- Draw a bracket ( ]) at the end of the last word the student reads in one minute.
- Words the student omits should be counted as errors, even if you prompt the student.
- Indicate with a caret extra words that have been inserted. If possible, write the inserted word. Count insertions as errors.
- Draw an arrow between words that have been reversed. Count these as one error.
- Students might repeat words on occasion. Do not count this behavior as an error.

Finding the Student's Accuracy Rate

To find a student's accuracy rate, count the total number of words read in one minute. The numbers beside the passage on the teacher's page will make this an easier task. Subtract the number of errors from the total number of words read and use that figure to find the number of correct words read per minute. Then divide the correct words per minute by the total number of words read to find the accuracy rate. Record these numbers on the Reading Rate and Accuracy chart located on your Oral Fluency Assessment pages.

- Record the student's score on the Oral Fluency Scores pages and the Student Assessment Record.
- Complete the Reading Fluency scale at the bottom of your Oral Fluency Assessment page. These qualitative measures indicate your subjective judgment of how the student compares with other students who are reading at grade level.

READING RATE AND ACCURACY	
Total Words Read:	130
Number of Errors:	19
Number of Correct Words Read Per Minute (WPM):	111
Accuracy Rate:	85%
(Number of Correct Words Read per Minute ÷ Total Words Read)	

READING FLUENCY	Low	Average	High
Decoding Ability	○	○	●
Pace	○	●	○
Syntax	○	●	○
Self-correction	○	●	○
Intonation	○	○	●

Interpreting the Oral Fluency Assessments

First, compare the student's number of correct words per minute with the following chart. This will give you an idea of how the student compares with other students in the same grade at the same time of year. The data in this chart represents the approximate number of correct words read per minute a student should be reading in Grades 2–6. The two rows of numbers represent the 50th and 75th percentiles.

	Units 1-2	Units 3-4	Units 5-6	
Grade 2	79	100	117	75th Percentile
	51	72	89	50th Percentile
Grade 3	99	120	137	75th Percentile
	71	92	107	50th Percentile
Grade 4	119	139	152	75th Percentile
	94	112	123	50th Percentile
Grade 5	139	156	168	75th Percentile
	110	127	139	50th Percentile
Grade 6	153	167	177	75th Percentile
	127	140	150	50th Percentile

Source Adapted from Hasbrouck, J., & Tindal, G. (2005). Oral Reading Fluency: 90 Years of Measurement (Tech. Rep. No. 33). Eugene, Oregon: University of Oregon, College of Education, Behavioral Research and Teaching.

Then examine the student's accuracy rate. Reading accuracy should remain constant or gradually increase within a grade and between grades, until it stabilizes at ninety percent or higher. You may find it helpful to compare a student's accuracy rate after each administration to ensure that it remains constant or increases.

Next, examine the types of errors the student is making and consider how they represent underlying student behaviors. Here are some examples:

• Inserting extra words suggests that the student understands what is read, is constructing meaning, but is reading somewhat impulsively.

• A student who refuses to attempt to read a word is probably uncertain of his or her abilities and is unwilling to take risks.

• Misreading regular letter sounds implies that the student has not yet mastered the conventions of the sound-symbol relationship. This is in contrast with the student who misreads complex letter sounds (alternate sounds, blends, diphthongs, digraphs, and so on) but has little difficulty with regular letter sounds.

Finally, consider the error pattern. If errors are scattered randomly throughout the passage, then the error types represent skills the student has not yet developed. If errors increase in frequency from beginning to end, then fatigue or inattention likely are involved.

Other Considerations

Several strategies are available for promoting reading fluency and accuracy. These involve pairing an accomplished reader with a developing reader, small-group choral reading, and repeated readings of familiar text.

You may find it useful to establish targets for reading accuracy. These targets may include goals such as reading ten words in a row without error, increasing by increments the number of correct words a student reads in a minute, or decreasing a specific error type. Establishing such targets allows you to provide appropriate instructional support and gives students a reasonable goal.

End of Unit Writing Prompt

The writing prompt offers the opportunity for an on-demand writing performance similar to the type students will encounter in high-stakes testing. Use the rubrics that follow the prompts to judge students' work. Student writing should be included in each student's Writing Portfolio.

Teacher Records

This Teacher's Edition contains record keeping material that will help you keep track of student progress in lesson assessments.

Six Point Rubrics

Six Point Writing Rubrics for assessing student writing are included.

These can take the place of the four point rubrics if you are in a school that uses the six point rubric system.

Oral Fluency Scores

These pages allow you to note student accuracy rates throughout the year.

Class Assessment Record

These pages offer a warehouse for class scores.

The spaces following the student's name allow for the recording of student scores in each lesson assessment (out of the 50-point scale) and each writing prompt (using the four point or six point rubrics to assess).

The format of the Class Assessment Record provides an easy way to monitor student growth across the year.

Student Assessment Record

You can duplicate this page for each student and use it to track student progress.

Comprehension Observation Log

Observing students as they read anthology selections is an effective way to learn their strengths and areas of need in comprehension. Use the Comprehension Observation Log to record your observations of students. Choose a small set of students to focus on for a particular lesson. You might want to observe students more than once to get a clear idea of their comprehension of texts. Copy this page for each student or group of students you observe.

Name _____ Date _____ Score _____

Rugby & Rosie

Vocabulary

Read each item. Fill in the bubble for the answer you think is correct.

1. A synonym for **chores** is

  Ⓐ games.   Ⓒ toys.

  🅑 jobs.   Ⓓ vacations.

2. If you are **grateful,** you are

  🅐 thankful.   Ⓒ helpful.

  Ⓑ careful.   Ⓓ hopeful.

3. The boy was **patient** with Rugby. This means the boy was

  Ⓐ playful.   Ⓒ friendly.

  Ⓑ quick-tempered. 🅓 willing to wait.

4. Rosie had a lot of **energy.** What does this mean?

  Ⓐ She learned quickly.

  Ⓑ She became a guide dog.

  🅒 She was very active.

  Ⓓ She liked everybody.

5. At first, Rugby tried to **ignore** Rosie. **Ignore** means

  Ⓐ sit close beside.

  Ⓑ run away from.

  Ⓒ look at.

  🅓 pay no attention to.

Rugby & Rosie (continued)

Comprehension

Read the following questions carefully. Then completely fill in the bubble of each correct answer. You may look back at the selection to find the answer to each of the questions.

1. Why does Rugby ignore Rosie at first?

   Ⓐ Rosie is not very friendly to him.

   Ⓑ He is used to being the only dog.

   Ⓒ He knows Rosie will not stay long.

   Ⓓ Rosie likes to play too much.

2. How does the new puppy act when she first arrives?

   Ⓐ full of energy

   Ⓑ quiet and calm

   Ⓒ cute but naughty

   Ⓓ a little bit afraid

Rugby & Rosie (continued)

3. After living with the boy's family for one year, Rosie

   Ⓐ finds a new family.

   Ⓑ decides to stay there.

   Ⓒ goes to a special school.

   Ⓓ becomes a dog trainer.

4. Who is Rosie with at the graduation?

   Ⓐ Rosie's puppy

   Ⓑ Rosie's teacher

   Ⓒ Rosie's parents

   Ⓓ Rosie's new owner

5. Why does Rugby not meet the boy at the bus stop one day?

   Ⓐ He is asleep on the porch with Rosie.

   Ⓑ He is waiting on the couch.

   Ⓒ He is in the kitchen eating.

   Ⓓ He is playing with Rosie in the back yard.

Rugby & Rosie (continued)

Read the following questions carefully. Use complete sentences to answer the questions. Possible answers below

6. How do you know this selection could really happen?

The people and animals seem real and the events could happen.

7. Why does the family take Rosie on trips to places such as the bank and the store?

They take her to places that people who are blind will need to go.

8. How does the boy know Rugby misses Rosie when she goes away?

Rugby looks all over for Rosie and whines when he cannot find her.

9. How does Rosie behave at the graduation?

Rosie is happy to see everyone, but she will not leave her owner's side.

10. How does Rugby greet the new puppy at the end of the selection?

Rugby is friendly to Blue and licks the puppy on the nose.

Rugby & Rosie (continued)

Read the question below. Write complete sentences for your answer. Support your answer with information from the selection.

Linking to the Concepts How do you think Rosie felt when she saw her old family at the graduation?

_____

_____

_____

_____

_____

Read the questions below. Your answer should be based on your own experience. Write complete sentences for your answer.

Personal Response Have you ever had to give away something that was very special to you? What was it, and why did you give it away?

_____

_____

_____

_____

_____

Rugby & Rosie (continued)

Grammar, Usage, and Mechanics

Read each question. Fill in the bubble beside the answer in each group that is correct. If none of the answers is correct, choose the last answer, "none of the above."

1. In which sentence is a noun underlined?

Ⓐ The strong wind <u>blew</u> the door closed.

Ⓑ <u>The</u> strong wind blew the door closed.

Ⓒ The strong wind blew the <u>door</u> closed.

Ⓓ none of the above

2. In which sentence is a noun underlined?

Ⓐ A <u>tall</u> tree grew near the school.

Ⓑ A tall tree grew <u>near</u> the school.

Ⓒ A tall tree <u>grew</u> near the school.

Ⓓ none of the above

3. In which sentence is a proper noun underlined?

Ⓐ Is your birthday in <u>May</u>?

Ⓒ Is <u>your</u> birthday in May?

Ⓑ Is your <u>birthday</u> in May?

Ⓓ none of the above

4. In which sentence is a proper noun underlined?

Ⓐ The <u>family</u> took a vacation trip to California.

Ⓑ The family took a vacation trip to <u>California</u>.

Ⓒ The family <u>took</u> a vacation trip to California.

Ⓓ none of the above

5. Which of these words is usually a noun?

Ⓐ chew

Ⓒ tall

Ⓑ shoe

Ⓓ none of the above

Rugby & Rosie (continued)

Analyzing the Selection

Read the questions below. Write complete sentences for your answer. Support your answer with information from the selection.

Why do you think the narrator remembers the particular incidents described in "Rugby & Rosie"? Why are certain family events in your life so easy to remember?

_____

_____

_____

_____

_____

_____

_____

_____

_____

_____

_____

_____

Rugby & Rosie (continued)

Oral Fluency Assessment

Birds of a Feather

Most birds have very light bones to make it easier for them	1–12
to fly. Large birds flap their wings slowly, while small birds	13–23
flap their wings very fast.	24–28
Hummingbirds are among the smallest birds. They beat their	29–37
wings very fast, fifty to eighty times every minute. Because	38–47
their wings flap so fast, they make a noise that sounds like	48–59
humming. That special sound is what gave hummingbirds	60–67
their name.	68–69
Many large birds do not need to flap their wings much. They	70–81
have big wings that let them glide through the air. When they	82–93
spread out their wings, they seem to float on the wind. Birds	94–105
like eagles and seagulls can glide for a long time.	106–115
Owls have wing feathers that let them fly fast and quietly.	116–126
Birds that dive for fish or catch animals need strong wings to	127–138
help them get back into the air. Each bird has special wings to	139–151
help it do what it needs to do.	152–159

EVALUATING CODES FOR ORAL FLUENCY

sky (/) words read incorrectly

blue
^ sky (^) inserted word
( ]) after the last word

READING RATE AND ACCURACY

Total Words Read: _____

Number of Errors: _____

Number of Correct Words
Read Per Minute (WPM): _____

Accuracy Rate: _____

(Number of Correct Words Read per
Minute ÷ Total Words Read)

READING FLUENCY

	Low	Average	High
Decoding ability	○	○	○
Pace	○	○	○
Syntax	○	○	○
Self-correction	○	○	○
Intonation	○	○	○

Record student rates on the Oral Fluency Scores pages.

Name _____ Date _____ Score _____

The Legend of Damon and Pythias

Vocabulary

Read each item. Fill in the bubble for the answer you think is correct.

1. **Miserable** means

   Ⓐ very unhappy.   Ⓒ very kind.

   Ⓑ very crowded   Ⓓ very happy.

2. All of these are compound words EXCEPT

   Ⓐ daytime.   Ⓒ popcorn.

   Ⓑ bathroom.   Ⓓ exchange.

3. Pythias **struggled** to free himself. This means he

   Ⓐ spoke aloud.

   Ⓑ wandered around.

   Ⓒ waited patiently.

   Ⓓ worked hard.

4. Damon had great **faith** in Pythias. In this sentence, **faith** means

   Ⓐ assistance.

   Ⓑ fortune.

   Ⓒ trust.

   Ⓓ concern.

5. Damon **persuaded** the king to let him take the place of Pythias. **Persuaded** means

   Ⓐ paid.   Ⓒ tricked.

   Ⓑ convinced.   Ⓓ flattered.

The Legend of Damon and Pythias (continued)

Comprehension

Read the following questions carefully. Then completely fill in the bubble of each correct answer. You may look back at the selection to find the answer to each of the questions.

1. The author wrote this selection in order to

  Ⓐ show how to take a stand against bad laws.

  Ⓑ explain how to change laws.

  Ⓒ convince the reader to make a new friend.

  Ⓓ tell a story about friendship.

2. What does Pythias do that leads to his arrest?

  Ⓐ He runs from a soldier.

  Ⓑ He speaks out against a new law.

  Ⓒ He rides a horse.

  Ⓓ He is attacked by robbers.

The Legend of Damon and Pythias (continued)

3. Who visits Pythias in prison?

    Ⓐ a friend

    Ⓑ a soldier

    Ⓒ the king

    Ⓓ his family

4. Pythias' return to the King is delayed by

    Ⓐ Damon.

    Ⓑ robbers.

    Ⓒ soldiers.

    Ⓓ the jailer.

5. The king sets Damon and Pythias free because

    Ⓐ the jailer had made a great mistake.

    Ⓑ the king has a great army to protect him.

    Ⓒ Damon and Pythias share a strong and true friendship.

    Ⓓ the king is afraid of the large crowd.

The Legend of Damon and Pythias (continued)

Read the following questions carefully. Use complete sentences to answer the questions. Possible answers below

6. What does Damon offer to do for Pythias?

Damon offers to stay in prison so Pythias can visit his family.

7. What do the robbers do to Pythias?

They take his money and tie him to a tree.

8. Just before Damon is about to die, how does he feel about Pythias?

Damon believes that if Pythias does not return, it is not his fault.

9. How does the king change in the selection?

In the beginning, he seems mean and harsh. By the end, he seems kinder.

10. At the end of the selection, what does the king say he would do to have a friend like Damon and Pythias?

He says that he would give all his money and power for one true friend.

The Legend of Damon and Pythias (continued)

Read the question below. Write complete sentences for your answer. Support your answer with information from the selection.

Linking to the Concepts How is true friendship like a treasure in this selection?

_____

_____

_____

_____

_____

_____

Read the questions below. Your answer should be based on your own experience. Write complete sentences for your answer.

Personal Response Are you a true friend to someone? How do you show that you are a true friend?

_____

_____

_____

_____

_____

_____

The Legend of Damon and Pythias (continued)

Grammar, Usage, and Mechanics

Read each question. Fill in the bubble beside the answer in each group that is correct. If none of the answers is correct, choose the last answer, "none of the above."

1. In which sentence is the verb underlined?

Ⓐ The <u>turtle</u> slid off the log.

Ⓑ The turtle slid off the <u>log</u>.

Ⓒ The turtle slid <u>off</u> the log.

Ⓓ none of the above

2. In which sentence is an action verb underlined?

Ⓐ A huge whale <u>swam</u> beside the boat.

Ⓑ Some people <u>were</u> on that side of the boat.

Ⓒ One of them <u>was</u> my cousin.

Ⓓ none of the above

3. In which sentence is a state-of-being verb underlined?

Ⓐ Walt <u>fed</u> the pony. Ⓒ A horse <u>walked</u> over.

Ⓑ He <u>was</u> hungry. Ⓓ none of the above

4. In which sentence is the verb phrase underlined?

Ⓐ The game will <u>start soon</u>.

Ⓑ My sister plays on <u>one of</u> the teams.

Ⓒ She <u>has scored</u> a goal before.

Ⓓ none of the above

5. Which of these is usually a verb?

Ⓐ rabbit **Ⓒ** hop

Ⓑ fur Ⓓ none of the above

The Legend of Damon and Pythias (continued)

Analyzing the Selection

Read the question below. Write complete sentences for your answer. Support your answer with information from the selection.

After the robbery, Pythias struggled greatly to get back to the king. Describe what he went through. What does this suggest about him and his feelings about friendship?

_____

_____

_____

_____

_____

_____

_____

_____

_____

_____

_____

_____

_____

The Legend of Damon and Pythias (continued)

Oral Fluency Assessment

Watch Out, Bug!

Most people know that frogs and birds eat bugs. But did you	1–12
know that some plants eat insects, too?	13–19
One plant that eats insects is the Venus flytrap. This is a	20–31
meat-eating plant with leaves that open wide. The leaves have	32–42
pads with tiny hairs on them. When an insect lands on one of	43–55
the open leaf pads, it brushes against the hairs. The leaf curls	56–67
up, snaps shut, and the insect is caught inside.	68–76
Another plant that catches insects is the pitcher plant. This	77–86
plant is partly full of liquid and has a lid on top. The sides of	87–101
the plant are slippery. When insects climb inside the plant, they	102–112
slide down the sides and can't get out of the liquid.	113–123
The sundew plant can also catch insects. It has hairs on its	124–135
leaves that are covered with something like glue. If an insect	136–146
lands on these hairs, it gets stuck. Then the sundew leaf folds	147–158
down, and the insect is trapped.	159–164

READING RATE AND ACCURACY

Total Words Read: _____

Number of Errors: _____

Number of Correct Words
Read Per Minute (WPM): _____

Accuracy Rate: _____

(Number of Correct Words Read per
Minute ÷ Total Words Read)

READING FLUENCY

	Low	Average	High
Decoding ability	○	○	○
Pace	○	○	○
Syntax	○	○	○
Self-correction	○	○	○
Intonation	○	○	○

Record student rates on the Oral Fluency Scores pages.

Name _____ Date _____ Score _____

Good-bye, 382 Shin Dang Dong

Vocabulary

Read each item. Fill in the bubble for the answer you think is correct.

1. What is the contraction for the words *did not?*

    Ⓐ did'nt   ●Ⓒ didn't

    Ⓑ didnot   Ⓓ di'nt

2. Peculiar is another word for

    ●Ⓐ strange.   Ⓒ young.

    Ⓑ ordinary.   Ⓓ wealthy.

3. She **insisted** that she liked her name. **Insisted** means

    Ⓐ explained.

    Ⓑ yelled.

    ●Ⓒ said firmly.

    Ⓓ said weakly.

4. Jangmi's parents were **enthusiastic** about America. **Enthusiastic** means

    Ⓐ surprised.

    ●Ⓑ excited.

    Ⓒ unsure.

    Ⓓ sad.

5. America was a **foreign** land. This means it was a

    ●Ⓐ different country.   Ⓒ large country.

    Ⓑ free country.   Ⓓ wealthy country.

Good-bye, 382 Shin Dang Dong (continued)

Comprehension

Read the following questions carefully. Then completely fill in the bubble of each correct answer. You may look back at the selection to find the answer to each of the questions.

1. During the monsoon season, the weather is mostly

    Ⓐ sunny.

    Ⓑ foggy.

    Ⓒ rainy.

    Ⓓ snowy.

2. Jangmi does not want to move because

    Ⓐ she does not want to leave Kisuni.

    Ⓑ she likes her school.

    Ⓒ she can not take her lovely things.

    Ⓓ her mother is staying in Korea.

Good-bye, 382 Shin Dang Dong (continued)

3. What fruit in America is like a chummy?

Ⓐ strawberry

Ⓑ grape

Ⓒ small yellow apple

Ⓓ honeydew melon

4. What do the Korean guests who come to the farewell lunch do first when they arrive?

Ⓐ They eat pastel rice cakes.

Ⓑ They take off their shoes.

Ⓒ They sing Korean songs.

Ⓓ They set up the table of food.

5. This selection is told from the

Ⓐ first-person point of view of Jangmi.

Ⓑ third-person point of view of the Korean guests.

Ⓒ second-person point of view.

Ⓓ first-person point of view of Kisuni.

Lesson 3

Good-bye, 382 Shin Dang Dong (continued)

Read the following questions carefully. Use complete sentences to answer the questions. Possible answers below

6. How is the time different in Korea and the United States?

When it is night in Korea, it is daytime in the United States.

7. How is heating a house different in the two countries?

In Korea, heat travels through ondal floors. Here, there are radiators.

8. How does Jangmi feel when she walks through the house in America?

She is sad and misses her old house. She wants to go back to Korea.

9. What foods do the American neighbors bring?

They bring casseroles, iced cakes, and a fruit bowl.

10. What does Jangmi do after the American guests leave?

She writes a letter to Kisuni.

Good-bye, 382 Shin Dang Dong (continued)

Read the question below. Write complete sentences for your answer. Support your answer with information from the selection.

Linking to the Concepts What helps Jangmi feel better about leaving her best friend?

_____

_____

_____

_____

_____

Read the prompt below. Your response should be based on your own experience. Write complete sentences for your response.

Personal Response Write about a time you made a new friend.

_____

_____

_____

_____

_____

_____

Good-bye, 382 Shin Dang Dong (continued)

Grammar, Usage, and Mechanics

Read each question. Fill in the bubble beside the answer in each group that is correct. If none of the answers is correct, choose the last answer, "none of the above."

1. In which sentence is the subject underlined?

Ⓐ He <u>filled</u> the hole.   ⓒ <u>He</u> filled the hole.

Ⓑ He filled the <u>hole</u>.   Ⓓ none of the above

2. Which sentence has a compound subject?

Ⓐ Big rocks are there.   ⓒ People like to climb.

Ⓑ A ball and bat were here.   Ⓓ none of the above

3. Which sentence has a compound predicate?

Ⓐ The bird landed and looked for some seeds.

Ⓑ The seeds were in the feeder on a pole.

ⓒ The pole makes it hard for squirrels.

Ⓓ none of the above

4. What is the best way to combine these two sentences?
Jan walked home. Peter walked home, too.

Ⓐ Jan walked home and Peter, too.

Ⓑ Jan walked home Peter walked home, too.

ⓒ Jan and Peter walked home.

Ⓓ none of the above

5. What is the best way to combine these two sentences?
The kitten purred. The kitten curled up on the couch.

Ⓐ The kitten purred, it curled up on the couch.

Ⓑ The kitten purred and curled up on the couch.

ⓒ The kitten purred so curled up on the couch.

Ⓓ none of the above

UNIT 1 Lesson 3

Good-bye, 382 Shin Dang Dong (continued)

Analyzing the Selection

Read the question below. Write complete sentences for your answer. Support your answer with information from the selections.

How are the selections "Rugby & Rosie" and "Good-bye, 382 Shin Dang Dong" alike, and how are they different? Focus on the characters, settings, and events in the selections.

_____

_____

_____

_____

_____

_____

_____

_____

_____

_____

_____

_____

_____

Goodbye, 382 Shin Dang Dong (continued)

Oral Fluency Assessment

Listen Up!

"Boy, does this sound silly."	1–5
John rolled his eyes at Kendra. They were walking home	6–15
after school talking about their homework this week. They	16–24
were supposed to listen for a total of two hours. They could do	25–37
it any time they wanted, for short times or long. They had to	38–50
listen and write down some of the things they heard. They also	51–62
had to describe where they listened and the time of day.	63–73
As they walked by a small corner park, Kendra stopped	74–83
for a moment. She said, "Hey, I have an idea. Let's start right	84–96
here. It's just about two-thirty, my parents won't be home for	97–108
two more hours, and neither will your mother. We should sit	109–119
down in the park and get part of the assignment done. It will	120–132
be easy."	133–134
John thought Kendra had a good idea. He spotted a bench	135–145
beside the fountain. "Let's get started," he said. "We can sit	146–156
over there."	157–158
After just a few seconds, Kendra began writing something	159–167
down. John followed right after her, and for the next half hour,	168–179
they did nothing but sit, listen, and take notes.	180–188

EVALUATING CODES FOR ORAL FLUENCY

sky   (/) words read incorrectly

blue
   ^   sky   (^) inserted word
            ( ]) after the last word

READING RATE AND ACCURACY

Total Words Read: _____

Number of Errors: _____

Number of Correct Words
Read Per Minute (WPM): _____

Accuracy Rate: _____

(Number of Correct Words Read per
Minute ÷ Total Words Read)

READING FLUENCY

	Low	Average	High
Decoding ability	○	○	○
Pace	○	○	○
Syntax	○	○	○
Self-correction	○	○	○
Intonation	○	○	○

Record student rates on the Oral Fluency Scores pages.

Name _____ Date _____ Score _____

Beauty and the Beast

Vocabulary

Read each item. Fill in the bubble for the answer you think is correct.

1. **Despair** means very great
   - Ⓐ kindness.
   - Ⓑ stillness.
   - ⬤Ⓒ sadness.
   - Ⓓ happiness.

2. The words *book, test,* and *student* best relate to
   - ⬤Ⓐ school.
   - Ⓑ sports.
   - Ⓒ farming.
   - Ⓓ family.

3. Beauty **clung** to her father. **Clung** means she
   - Ⓐ looked at him.
   - Ⓑ spoke to him.
   - ⬤Ⓒ held him tight.
   - Ⓓ moved near him.

4. The dress Beauty wore was **magnificent.** It was very
   - Ⓐ unusual.
   - ⬤Ⓑ beautiful.
   - Ⓒ new.
   - Ⓓ expensive.

5. Beauty was surprised at the **splendor** of the castle. **Splendor** is
   - Ⓐ flowers and trees.
   - Ⓑ food and drink.
   - Ⓒ bricks and stones.
   - ⬤Ⓓ beauty or riches.

Beauty and the Beast (continued)

Comprehension

Read the following questions carefully. Then completely fill in the bubble of each correct answer. You may look back at the selection to find the answer to each of the questions.

1. When her father's only remaining ship came in, Beauty asked for

Ⓐ new jewels.

Ⓑ beautiful dresses.

Ⓒ one rose.

Ⓓ more food.

2. What is strange about the castle Beauty's father finds?

Ⓐ No one is there.

Ⓑ It is huge.

Ⓒ The grounds are beautiful.

Ⓓ The owner is unkind.

Beauty and the Beast (continued)

3. What does the Beast ask Beauty every night at dinner?

Ⓐ Did you like your rose?

Ⓑ Do I look ugly?

Ⓒ Will your sisters visit?

Ⓓ Will you marry me?

4. How could Beauty get back to the Beast's castle?

Ⓐ walk through the gardens

Ⓑ turn the ring on her finger

Ⓒ take a carriage ride

Ⓓ tell the Beast that she would marry him

5. When Beauty stayed too long with her sisters, the Beast

Ⓐ sent Beauty a rose.

Ⓑ came to visit too.

Ⓒ almost died.

Ⓓ hurt Beauty's father.

Beauty and the Beast (continued)

Read the following questions carefully. Use complete sentences to answer the questions. Possible answers below

6. How is Beauty different from her sisters?

She is prettier, kinder, smarter, and more helpful. She likes reading too.

7. What does Beauty dream about during her first night in the castle?

She dreams about a fairy who tells her she will get a reward.

8. What would happen to the Beast if Beauty did not come back from her visit home?

The Beast would die if she did not come back in one week.

9. Why do Beauty's sisters try to keep her longer than a week when she comes for a visit?

They are jealous and want to make Beauty break her promise to the Beast.

10. What three things happen right after Beauty agrees to marry the Beast?

Lights blaze, music fills the air, and the Beast turns into a Prince.

Beauty and the Beast (continued)

Read the question below. Write complete sentences for your answer. Support your answer with information from the selection.

Linking to the Concepts How do Beauty's feelings about the Beast change during the selection?

_____

_____

_____

_____

_____

Read the questions below. Your answer should be based on your own experience. Write complete sentences for your answer.

Personal Response Have you ever changed your mind about another person? What happened that made you feel different?

_____

_____

_____

_____

_____

Beauty and the Beast (continued)

Grammar, Usage, and Mechanics

Read each question. Fill in the bubble beside the answer in each group that is correct. If none of the answers is correct, choose the last answer, "none of the above."

1. Which of these is a sentence fragment?

Ⓐ A branch had fallen from the tree.

Ⓑ Dad looked around the yard.

Ⓒ Hearing a loud noise outside.

Ⓓ none of the above

2. Which of these is a complete sentence, not a fragment?

Ⓐ Busy all day.

Ⓒ The weekend tennis.

Ⓑ This week went quickly.

Ⓓ none of the above

3. Which of these is a complete sentence, not a fragment?

Ⓐ A small bench near the top.

Ⓒ Walking up the tall hill.

Ⓑ Three of us after school.

Ⓓ none of the above

4. Which sentence has a compound subject?

Ⓐ Cars and trucks crossed the bridge.

Ⓑ A boat waited for it to go up.

Ⓒ The bridge slowly opened up.

Ⓓ none of the above

5. Which sentence has a compound predicate?

Ⓐ This basketball game would take place out of town.

Ⓑ The players left the school and walked to the bus.

Ⓒ Many of the parents followed in their own cars.

Ⓓ none of the above

Beauty and the Beast (continued)

Analyzing the Selection

Read the questions below. Write complete sentences for your answer. Support your answer with information from the selection.

What makes "Beauty and the Beast" a fairy tale? How do the characters behave like real characters, even though this is a fairy tale?

_____

_____

_____

_____

_____

_____

_____

_____

_____

_____

_____

_____

Beauty and the Beast (continued)

Oral Fluency Assessment

Suzie and "Buddy"

"This is so different from home," said Suzie. She smiled	1–10
at her younger brother and walked toward the creek. The	11–20
family was on a camping trip. This was their first morning in	21–32
the forest.	33–34
Luis ran to catch up with Suzie and held her hand. Both	35–46
were wearing heavy sweaters to keep warm in the chilly	47–56
morning air.	57–58
They sat down on a boulder beside the mountain stream.	59–68
Across the stream was a meadow. Beyond that was the rocky	69–79
base of a huge mountain. They were surrounded by mountains.	80–89
Many of the mountains still had snow on them.	90–98
"Look, Suzie, cows." Luis pointed at several animals that had	99–108
wandered into the meadow.	109–112
"I don't think they are cows, Buddy. They look like elk. I think	113–125
they are almost like deer, but bigger."	126–132
Luis snuggled closer to his sister. He loved it when she called	133–144
him "Buddy." He thought she was the smartest person in the	145–155
world, or at least the smartest kid. He knew this was going to	156–168
be a wonderful camping trip.	169–173

EVALUATING CODES FOR ORAL FLUENCY

sky   (/) words read incorrectly

blue
^ sky (^) inserted word
        ( ]) after the last word

READING RATE AND ACCURACY

Total Words Read: _____

Number of Errors: _____

Number of Correct Words
Read Per Minute (WPM): _____

Accuracy Rate: _____

(Number of Correct Words Read per
Minute ÷ Total Words Read)

READING FLUENCY

	Low	Average	High
Decoding ability	O	O	O
Pace	O	O	O
Syntax	O	O	O
Self-correction	O	O	O
Intonation	O	O	O

Record student rates on the Oral Fluency Scores pages.

Name _____ Date _____ Score _____

Teammates

Vocabulary

Read each item. Fill in the bubble for the answer you think is correct.

1. An antonym for **possess** is

    Ⓐ lose.   Ⓒ break.

    Ⓑ chase.   Ⓓ own.

2. Responded is the same as

    Ⓐ exited.   Ⓒ changed.

    Ⓑ answered.   Ⓓ visited.

3. Some **opponents** called Jackie Robinson mean names. Who are **opponents?**

    Ⓐ umpires

    Ⓑ owners of a team

    Ⓒ fans in the stands

    Ⓓ players on the other team

4. Jackie showed the other players he was **equal** to them. **Equal** means

    Ⓐ as good as.   Ⓒ star player.

    Ⓑ best friend.   Ⓓ not afraid.

5. African American and white people played in different baseball **leagues.** What are **leagues?**

    Ⓐ positions on a team   Ⓒ rules

    Ⓑ groups of teams   Ⓓ stadiums

Teammates (continued)

Comprehension

Read the following questions carefully. Then completely fill in the bubble of each correct answer. You may look back at the selection to find the answer to each of the questions.

1. During earlier times, there were baseball leagues for African American players and baseball leagues for white players. What were the leagues called?

  Ⓐ the Major Leagues and the Minor Leagues

  Ⓑ the National League and the American League

  Ⓒ the Negro Leagues and the Major Leagues

  Ⓓ the Negro Leagues and the Minor Leagues

2. Why did the players in the Negro Leagues carry their own food?

  Ⓐ They always seemed to be hungry.

  Ⓑ Some restaurants would not serve them.

  Ⓒ They had to travel to distant places.

  Ⓓ Many of them ate special food.

Teammates (continued)

3. Who was Branch Rickey?

    Ⓐ the owner of the Brooklyn Dodgers

    Ⓑ a fan of the Brooklyn Dodgers

    Ⓒ a player for the Brooklyn Dodgers

    Ⓓ the general manager of the Brooklyn Dodgers

4. What is this selection mostly about?

    Ⓐ why people like the Dodgers so much

    Ⓑ the first African American player in major
league baseball

    Ⓒ how Pee Wee Reese became a star

    Ⓓ how many good players were in the Negro Leagues

5. Which word best describes Reese?

    Ⓐ loyal

    Ⓑ jealous

    Ⓒ angry

    Ⓓ funny

Teammates (continued)

Read the following questions carefully. Use complete sentences to answer the questions. Possible answers below

6. Why did Jackie Robinson promise not to fight back?

He knew fighting would keep African American players out of the Majors.

7. Why did Reese stand beside Robinson?

Reese stood beside him because Robinson was his teammate.

8. What was the signing of Robinson known as?

The signing of Robinson was known as "the great experiment."

9. Why did Rickey sign Robinson?

Rickey wanted the best players and did not care about race.

10. How were the players in the two leagues treated differently?

Only the major league players were paid well, ate well, and were famous.

Teammates (continued)

Read the question below. Write complete sentences for your answer. Support your answer with information from the selection.

Linking to the Concepts How did Reese prove he was a true friend?

_____

_____

_____

_____

_____

Read the question below. Your answer should be based on your own experience. Write complete sentences for your answer.

Personal Response When have you had to stick up for a friend? Explain what happened.

_____

_____

_____

_____

_____

Teammates (continued)

Grammar, Usage, and Mechanics

Read each question. Fill in the bubble beside the answer in each group that is correct. If none of the answers is correct, choose the last answer, "none of the above."

1. Which sentence has correct punctuation?

Ⓐ He asked Do you want soup?"

Ⓑ He asked, "Do you want soup?"

Ⓒ He asked, Do you want soup?

Ⓓ none of the above

2. Which sentence has correct punctuation?

Ⓐ The title of the chapter is "The Big Game."

Ⓑ The "title" of the chapter is The Big Game.

Ⓒ The title of the "chapter" is The Big Game.

Ⓓ none of the above

3. Which sentence has correct punctuation?

Ⓐ We swim fish, and sail.

Ⓒ We swim, fish, and sail.

Ⓑ We swim fish and sail.

Ⓓ none of the above

4. Which sentence has a mistake in punctuation?

Ⓐ "This is the right road," said Mom.

Ⓑ Dad asked when do we turn?

Ⓒ Mona answered, "Just a few blocks ahead."

Ⓓ none of the above

5. Which sentence has a mistake in punctuation?

Ⓐ The store sold shoes, boots, and, sandals.

Ⓑ They were stored in bags, boxes, and bins.

Ⓒ The store also sold shirts, sweaters, and jackets.

Ⓓ none of the above

UNIT 1 Lesson 5

Teammates (continued)

Analyzing the Selection

Read the question below. Write complete sentences for your answer. Support your answer with information from the selections.

Think about the selections in this unit. What is the most important lesson you learned about friendship? Explain what the lesson is and why it is so important.

_____

_____

_____

_____

_____

_____

_____

_____

_____

_____

_____

_____

UNIT 1 **Lesson 5**

Teammates (continued)

Oral Fluency Assessment

A Special Kite

It was a beautiful spring day. The sky was blue and there	1–12
was a nice breeze. In the park, many children were flying	13–23
their kites.	24–25
Carl walked to the park with his parents and his sister.	26–36
Under his arm was a special kite that had been sent to him	37–49
from Japan. His brother was in the army there. Carl missed his	50–60
brother and was excited about the kite.	61–68
Carl took the kite out. It was shaped like a fish. Carl thought	69–80
it was beautiful! He tied the string to the kite carefully so he	81–92
would not lose it. Then he held the kite high and let the breeze	93–107
take it into the sky.	108–113
As Carl let the string out, the kite flew higher. All the	114–125
other children noticed it, and they pulled their kites down so	126–136
they could see his kite better. After a while, his kite was the	137–149
only one in the sky.	150–154
All the children wanted to know where Carl got his kite.	155–165
When he told them, it made him proud and happy. His beautiful	166–177
kite helped him remember his brother who was far away.	178–187

**EVALUATING CODES
FOR ORAL FLUENCY**

sky   (/) words read incorrectly

blue
^   sky   (^) inserted word
           ( ]) after the last word

READING RATE AND ACCURACY

Total Words Read: _____

Number of Errors: _____

Number of Correct Words
Read Per Minute (WPM):   _____

Accuracy Rate: _____

(Number of Correct Words Read per
Minute ÷ Total Words Read)

READING FLUENCY

	Low	Average	High
Decoding ability	○	○	○
Pace	○	○	○
Syntax	○	○	○
Self-correction	○	○	○
Intonation	○	○	○

Record student rates on the Oral Fluency Scores pages.

Name _____ Date _____ Score _____

Narrative Writing

Writing Situation

A person who became your friend

Audience

Students your age

Directions for Writing

Friendship happens in different ways. Think about your friends and how you became friends. Write a story explaining how you became friends with one person. Include enough details so the reader will understand what happened.

Checklist

You will earn the best score if you

- think about the person you will write about before you begin.
- write in a way that is interesting to your readers.
- introduce the main characters early in the story.
- use describing words to tell about you and the person.
- tell events in the order they happen.
- vary the length and types of sentences.
- use subjects, verbs, and modifiers correctly.
- use words that tell how you feel about the person.
- choose words that mean what you want to say.
- read your writing after you finish and check for mistakes.

Four Point Rubrics for Narrative Writing

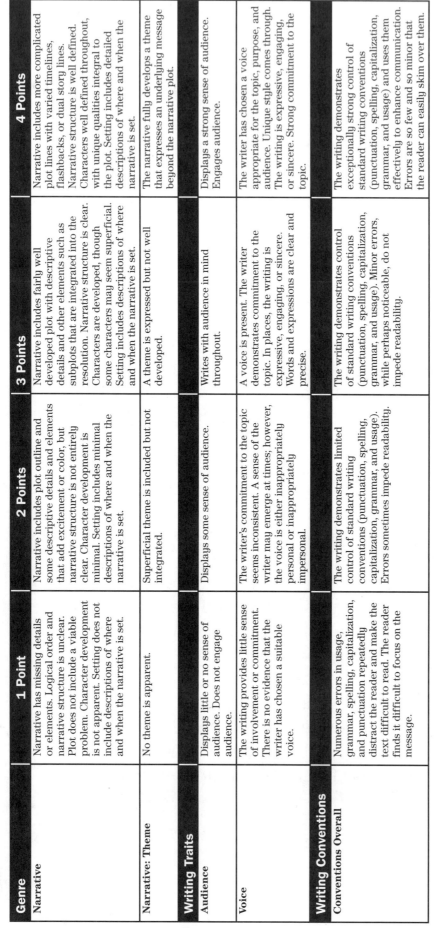

Genre	1 Point	2 Points	3 Points	4 Points
Narrative	Narrative has missing details or elements. Logical order and narrative structure is unclear. Plot does not include a viable problem. Character development is not apparent. Setting does not include descriptions of where and when the narrative is set.	Narrative includes plot outline and some descriptive details and elements that add excitement or color, but narrative structure is not entirely clear. Character development is minimal. Setting includes minimal descriptions of where and when the narrative is set.	Narrative includes fairly well developed plot with descriptive details and other elements such as subplots that are integrated into the resolution. Narrative structure is clear. Characters are developed, though some characters may seem superficial. Setting includes descriptions of where and when the narrative is set.	Narrative includes more complicated plot lines with varied timelines, flashbacks, or dual story lines. Narrative structure is well defined. Characters well defined throughout, with unique qualities integral to the plot. Setting includes detailed descriptions of where and when the narrative is set.
Narrative: Theme	No theme is apparent.	Superficial theme is included but not integrated.	A theme is expressed but not well developed.	The narrative fully develops a theme that expresses an underlying message beyond the narrative plot.
Writing Traits				
Audience	Displays little or no sense of audience. Does not engage audience.	Displays some sense of audience.	Writes with audience in mind throughout.	Displays a strong sense of audience. Engages audience.
Voice	The writing provides little sense of involvement or commitment. There is no evidence that the writer has chosen a suitable voice.	The writer's commitment to the topic seems inconsistent. A sense of the writer may emerge at times; however, the voice is either inappropriately personal or impersonal.	A voice is present. The writer demonstrates commitment to the topic. In places, the writing is expressive, engaging, or sincere. Words and expressions are clear and precise.	The writer has chosen a voice appropriate for the topic, purpose, and audience. Unique style comes through. The writing is expressive, engaging, or sincere. Strong commitment to the topic.
Writing Conventions				
Conventions Overall	Numerous errors in usage, grammar, spelling, capitalization, and punctuation repeatedly distract the reader and make the text difficult to read. The reader finds it difficult to focus on the message.	The writing demonstrates limited control of standard writing conventions (punctuation, spelling, capitalization, grammar, and usage). Errors sometimes impede readability.	The writing demonstrates control of standard writing conventions (punctuation, spelling, capitalization, grammar, and usage). Minor errors, while perhaps noticeable, do not impede readability.	The writing demonstrates exceptionally strong control of standard writing conventions (punctuation, spelling, capitalization, grammar, and usage) and uses them effectively to enhance communication. Errors are so few and so minor that the reader can easily skim over them.

Name _____ Date _____ Score _____

One Small Place in a Tree

Vocabulary

Read each item. Fill in the bubble for the answer you think is correct.

1. **Swarming** is moving in a large

   (A) tree.   (C) vehicle.

   (B) area.   (D) group.

2. Each of the following is a regular plural EXCEPT

   (A) babies.   (C) mice.

   (B) foxes.   (D) bugs.

3. A **hollow** tree is a home for animals. **Hollow** means it has

   (A) a hole inside.   (C) gray bark.

   (B) big branches.   (D) green leaves.

4. Woodpeckers are tree **dwellers.** This means they

   (A) eat in trees.

   (B) live in trees.

   (C) peck at trees.

   (D) fly from trees.

5. Squirrels **stored** nuts in trees. **Stored** means

   (A) found.

   (B) looked for.

   (C) ate.

   (D) put away.

One Small Place in a Tree (continued)

Comprehension

Read the following questions carefully. Then completely fill in the bubble of each correct answer. You may look back at the selection to find the answer to each of the questions.

1. Which animal in the selection sharpens its claws on a tree?

   Ⓐ owl

   Ⓑ woodpecker

   Ⓒ black bear

   Ⓓ squirrel

2. When chips of bark fall off a tree,

   Ⓐ timber beetles move into the tree.

   Ⓑ the tree dies right away.

   Ⓒ squirrels play in the bark.

   Ⓓ woodpeckers take the bark for nests.

One Small Place in a Tree (continued)

3. What do woodpeckers use to catch timber beetles?

Ⓐ their sharp beaks and long tongues

Ⓑ their sharp claws

Ⓒ their wing feathers

Ⓓ their sharp claws and long beaks

4. Who uses the hole in the tree after the squirrel?

Ⓐ bluebirds

Ⓑ woodpeckers

Ⓒ bears

Ⓓ beetles

5. The author wrote this selection in order to

Ⓐ persuade readers that trees are not as important as animals.

Ⓑ tell a funny story about forest animals.

Ⓒ explain how a tree can be a home to many animals.

Ⓓ show readers how to save a forest.

One Small Place in a Tree (continued)

Read the following questions carefully. Use complete sentences to answer the questions. Possible answers below

6. What do timber beetles do to the tree?

They bore holes into the tree. They also plant fungi to eat.

7. What sound brings red-bellied woodpeckers to the tree?

Woodpeckers hear the timber beetles chewing wood and come to the tree.

8. How would a flying squirrel use the hole in the tree?

A flying squirrel would store nuts in the hole and sleep there in winter.

9. According to the selection, how can trees get tree rot?

After animals have made a hole, bacteria can come in and cause tree rot.

10. What animals might live in a log after the tree falls?

Garter snakes, salamanders, and hammock spiders might live there.

One Small Place in a Tree (continued)

Read the question below. Write complete sentences for your answer. Support your answer with information from the selection.

Linking to the Concepts For which animal is the tree more important, the bluebird or the flying squirrel? Explain why.

_____

_____

_____

_____

_____

Read the questions below. Your answer should be based on your own experience. Write complete sentences for your answer.

Personal Response How is your home like the animals' home in the tree? How is it different?

_____

_____

_____

_____

_____

One Small Place in a Tree (continued)

Grammar, Usage, and Mechanics

Read each question. Fill in the bubble beside the answer in each group that is correct. If none of the answers is correct, choose the last answer, "none of the above."

1. Which sentence has a possessive noun?

Ⓐ Evelyn was looking under the bed.

Ⓑ The toy was a gift from Uncle Nick.

Ⓒ Jamey found his sister's toy.

Ⓓ none of the above

2. Which sentence has a possessive pronoun?

Ⓐ The book is about science.

Ⓑ Sam was reading his book.

Ⓒ He put it on the table beside the couch.

Ⓓ none of the above

3. Which sentence has correct punctuation?

Ⓐ Jeff's camera is new.   Ⓒ Jeffs' camera is new.

Ⓑ Jeffs camera is new.   Ⓓ none of the above

4. Which item has correct punctuation?

Ⓐ five student's projects   Ⓒ five students projects

Ⓑ five students project's   **Ⓓ** none of the above

5. Which word can take the place of the underlined part?

Many people admire <u>grandmother's</u> flowers.

Ⓐ theirs   Ⓒ she

Ⓑ her   Ⓓ none of the above

One Small Place in a Tree (continued)

Analyzing the Selection

Read the questions below. Write complete sentences for your answer. Support your answer with information from the selection.

Do you think the tree is more important when it is alive or dead? Should forests be cleared of dead trees, or should they be allowed to stay?

_____

_____

_____

_____

_____

_____

_____

_____

_____

_____

_____

_____

One Small Place in a Tree (continued)

Oral Fluency Assessment

The Watchdog

Ruff wanted to be a watchdog more than anything else. The	1–11
other puppies wanted to be pets, but not Ruff. He wanted to	12–23
find a family to protect.	24–28
One day a family with two children came in to adopt a dog.	29–41
The boy and girl loved Ruff right away. The father said they	42–53
needed a watchdog, and Ruff might grow up to be a big dog.	54–66
Ruff had a new home.	67–71
The family gave Ruff a doghouse, a dish, and a big yard to	72–84
watch. Ruff was as happy as a dog could be.	85–94
Most of the time, Ruff stayed in the house with the family.	95–106
At night, he stayed in his doghouse if the weather was good.	107–118
One night, Ruff sniffed the air and smelled smoke. Ruff	119–128
knew this was dangerous. He barked and barked. He ran to the	129–140
house and jumped on the door and barked again. The people	141–151
came out. They smelled the smoke and saw the fire. They	152–162
were all happy Ruff had kept barking. Ruff had become a real	163–174
watchdog, and his family loved him more than ever.	175–183

EVALUATING CODES FOR ORAL FLUENCY

sky   (/) words read incorrectly

blue
^ sky   (^) inserted word
      ( ]) after the last word

READING RATE AND ACCURACY

Total Words Read: _____

Number of Errors: _____

Number of Correct Words Read Per Minute (WPM): _____

Accuracy Rate: _____

(Number of Correct Words Read per Minute ÷ Total Words Read)

READING FLUENCY

	Low	Average	High
Decoding ability	○	○	○
Pace	○	○	○
Syntax	○	○	○
Self-correction	○	○	○
Intonation	○	○	○

Record student rates on the Oral Fluency Scores pages.

Name _____ Date _____ Score _____

Make Way for Ducklings

Vocabulary

Read each item. Fill in the bubble for the answer you think is correct.

1. Another word for **strange** is

Ⓐ unusual.   Ⓒ busy.

Ⓑ wet.   Ⓓ outside.

2. Each of the following is an irregular plural EXCEPT

Ⓐ sheep.   Ⓒ teeth.

Ⓑ women.   Ⓓ ships.

3. When ducklings **hatch,** they

Ⓐ learn to swim.   Ⓒ come out of eggs.

Ⓑ flap their wings.   Ⓓ make a funny sound.

4. The bird on the boat was **enormous.** This means the bird was

Ⓐ a funny color.

Ⓑ very large.

Ⓒ very noisy.

Ⓓ able to fly.

5. The police officer **beckoned** to Mrs. Mallard. This means he

Ⓐ waved her on.

Ⓑ waited on her.

Ⓒ whistled at her.

Ⓓ showed her the water.

Make Way for Ducklings (continued)

Comprehension

Read the following questions carefully. Then completely fill in the bubble of each correct answer. You may look back at the selection to find the answer to each of the questions.

1. What are Mr. and Mrs. Mallard looking for at the beginning of the selection?

    Ⓐ a flock of ducks

    Ⓑ a good place to live

    Ⓒ a police officer

    Ⓓ a place to cross the street

2. What do the ducks eat for breakfast after the first night at the Boston Public Garden?

    Ⓐ peanuts

    Ⓑ corn

    Ⓒ weeds

    Ⓓ berries

Make Way for Ducklings (continued)

3. Which of these could happen in real life?

Ⓐ ducks asking for different kinds of food

Ⓑ ducks building a bridge across a road

Ⓒ ducks telling people how they feel

Ⓓ ducks building a nest on an island in a river

4. Why does Mrs. Mallard stop visiting Michael, the policeman?

Ⓐ She is afraid of the cars on the road.

Ⓑ She was too tired to swim to the park.

Ⓒ She had to take care of the eggs.

Ⓓ She found another person to feed her.

5. What made Mr. and Mrs. Mallard burst with pride?

Ⓐ They swam to the park.

Ⓑ The ducklings hatched.

Ⓒ The police officer fed them.

Ⓓ The cars stopped for them.

Make Way for Ducklings (continued)

Read the following questions carefully. Use complete sentences to answer the questions. Possible answers below

6. What happens when Mrs. Mallard and her ducklings leave the river to go to the Public Garden?

   They have to cross a busy street, and the cars honk, but they do not stop.

7. How do the ducks finally get across the street?

   Michael and the other police officers stop the traffic for the ducks.

8. What could the birds do and not do when they molted?

   They were not able to fly, but they were still able to swim.

9. How did the people react to the Mallards waddling down the street?

   They stopped and stared. They thought it was amazing, cute, or nice.

10. How do you know that Mrs. Mallard and the ducklings were grateful to the police officers?

    When they got into the Public Garden, they stopped to say thank you.

Make Way for Ducklings (continued)

Read the question below. Write complete sentences for your answer. Support your answer with information from the selection.

Linking to the Concepts Why is the island a good city home for the Mallards?

_____

_____

_____

_____

_____

Read the questions below. Your answer should be based on your own experience. Write complete sentences for your answer.

Personal Response Is there a place near where you live that would make a good home for mallards? Why?

_____

_____

_____

_____

_____

_____

Make Way for Ducklings (continued)

Grammar, Usage, and Mechanics

Read each question. Fill in the bubble beside the answer in each group that is correct. If none of the answers is correct, choose the last answer, "none of the above."

1. In which sentence is the underlined plural word correct?

Ⓐ I have two <u>pillowes</u>.   Ⓒ I have two <u>pillow's</u>.

Ⓑ I have two <u>pillows</u>.   Ⓓ none of the above

2. In which sentence is the underlined plural word correct?

Ⓐ Dad used <u>matches</u> to start the campfire.

Ⓑ Dad used <u>matchs</u> to start the campfire.

Ⓒ Dad used <u>matcheses</u> to start the campfire.

Ⓓ none of the above

3. In which sentence is the underlined plural word correct?

Ⓐ Many big <u>citys</u> have a city council.

Ⓑ Many big <u>cities</u> have a city council.

Ⓒ Many big <u>cityes</u> have a city council.

Ⓓ none of the above

4. Which underlined plural word is incorrect?

Ⓐ Heavy snow knocked some <u>wires</u> down.

Ⓑ Mom made brown <u>beans</u> and cornbread.

Ⓒ The light <u>switchs</u> are made of plastic.

Ⓓ none of the above

5. Which underlined plural word is incorrect?

Ⓐ My friend's <u>kitties</u> like to play with string.

Ⓑ Two <u>calfs</u> stood beside the barn.

Ⓒ Sheri's running <u>shoes</u> are muddy.

Ⓓ none of the above

Make Way for Ducklings (continued)

Analyzing the Selection

Read the questions below. Write complete sentences for your answer. Support your answer with information from the selection.

In this selection, some of the people were helpful to the ducks, but some were not. Do you think it is important to help animals like the Mallards? Why?

_____

_____

_____

_____

_____

_____

_____

_____

_____

_____

_____

Make Way for Ducklings (continued)

Oral Fluency Assessment

The Jacket

Tim looked at his younger sister and sighed. Sammie had	1–10
taken off her coat again. Now she was running around the	11–21
playground wearing just a sweater. It had been hard to get	22–32
the coat on her in the first place. Tim was not looking forward	33–45
to doing it again. But since he was babysitting, it was his job.	46–58
"Sammie, you need your jacket," Tim said.	59–65
"I don't want to!" Sammie answered, slowly walking back	66–74
to him.	75–76
Tim stayed calm. "Look at me. I'm wearing my jacket to	77–87
stay warm."	88–89
"But I'm not cold," Sammie pouted. "Feel my skin." Tim put	90–100
his hand against her arm. He had to admit she was warm.	101–112
Tim wondered if Sammie did not get cold as easily as he did.	113–125
Plus, she was running around a lot. Maybe she was warm from	126–137
all the exercise.	138–140
Tim asked, "What if you do get cold?"	141–148
Sammie quickly said, "I'll come put my coat on."	149–157
"Okay," said Tim, and he watched Sammie go climb on	158–167
the bars. Then Tim smiled and thought, "Hey, I used to hate	168–179
wearing my jacket too!"	180–183

EVALUATING CODES FOR ORAL FLUENCY

sky (/) words read incorrectly

blue
^ sky (^) inserted word
( ]) after the last word

READING RATE AND ACCURACY

Total Words Read: _____

Number of Errors: _____

Number of Correct Words Read Per Minute (WPM): _____

Accuracy Rate: _____

(Number of Correct Words Read per Minute ÷ Total Words Read)

READING FLUENCY

	Low	Average	High
Decoding ability	O	O	O
Pace	O	O	O
Syntax	O	O	O
Self-correction	O	O	O
Intonation	O	O	O

Record student rates on the Oral Fluency Scores pages.

Name _____ Date _____ Score _____

Wolf Island

Vocabulary

Read each item. Fill in the bubble for the answer you think is correct.

1. Mild is another word for

  Ⓐ calm.   © young.

  Ⓑ strong.   Ⓓ fast.

2. Which homograph fits best in both sentences?

I heard the dog _____ earlier.

The _____ on the tree is dark brown.

  Ⓐ snarl   © wake

  Ⓑ bark   Ⓓ stick

3. A **layer** of snow covered the ground. A **layer** is

  Ⓐ a mound.   © a ball.

  Ⓑ a flake.   Ⓓ a coating.

4. The **population** changed without the wolves.
A **population** is all the animals that

  Ⓐ eat only plants.   © live in a place.

  Ⓑ eat other animals. Ⓓ have no shelter.

5. The wolf cubs' parents went **aboard** the raft. This
means they

  Ⓐ went off the raft.

  Ⓑ went on the raft.

  © went under the raft.

  Ⓓ went over the raft.

Wolf Island (continued)

Comprehension

Read the following questions carefully. Then completely fill in the bubble of each correct answer. You may look back at the selection to find the answer to each of the questions.

1. Which of these is a real thing wolves do?

   Ⓐ make rafts to float on a lake

   Ⓑ hunt deer for food

   Ⓒ talk to people or other animals

   Ⓓ raise crops for other animals

2. When the cubs howled from the raft, their parents

   Ⓐ howled back to them.

   Ⓑ swam out to them.

   Ⓒ did not hear them.

   Ⓓ kept on eating.

Wolf Island (continued)

3. How did the deer get food in winter?

Ⓐ dug under the snow

Ⓑ caught fish in the river

Ⓒ ate what they had stored

Ⓓ stole other animals' food

4. When the deer ate most of the grass, all of these animals had less to eat EXCEPT

Ⓐ mice.

Ⓑ owls.

Ⓒ foxes.

Ⓓ wolves.

5. Which of these sentences is an opinion from the selection?

Ⓐ Living trees are important.

Ⓑ The island had meadows.

Ⓒ The raft was made of logs.

Ⓓ Squirrels collected nuts.

Wolf Island (continued)

Read the following questions carefully. Use complete sentences to answer the questions. Possible answers below

6. After the wolves were gone, what happened to the deer?

   <u>With no wolves to eat them, there were too many deer for the amount of food.</u>

7. When more deer ate grass, what happened to the rabbits?

   <u>There was less grass for the rabbits, and fewer bunnies were born.</u>

8. What happened when food was hard to find in winter?

   <u>Animals got weaker and some died. Deer gnawed bark, and trees died.</u>

9. What problem did the wolves have after they landed on the mainland?

   <u>Other wolf families lived there, and they did not want to share food with them.</u>

10. How did the wolves' return to the island help the other animals?

    <u>The wolves ate the sick and weak deer and restored the needed balance.</u>

Wolf Island (continued)

Read the question below. Write complete sentences for your answer. Support your answer with information from the selection.

Linking to the Concepts What happens to a habitat when an important animal is removed?

_____

_____

_____

_____

_____

Read the questions below. Your answer should be based on your own experience. Write complete sentences for your answer.

Personal Response How did you feel when the adult wolves got on the raft and it landed on the mainland? What made you feel that way?

_____

_____

_____

_____

_____

Wolf Island (continued)

Grammar, Usage, and Mechanics

Read each question. Fill in the bubble beside the answer in each group that is correct. If none of the answers is correct, choose the last answer, "none of the above."

1. Which of these is a declarative sentence?

   Ⓐ Where is the pond?   Ⓒ I'll race you!

   🅑 The park closes at dark.   Ⓓ none of the above

2. Which of these is an interrogative sentence?

   Ⓐ The big box is for Grandma.

   Ⓑ Write Grandma's address on the package.

   🅒 When will the post office open?

   Ⓓ none of the above

3. Which of these is an exclamatory sentence?

   🅐 Watch out, that glass is sharp!

   Ⓑ How did the glass get broken?

   Ⓒ A few pieces of glass are on the floor.

   Ⓓ none of the above

4. Which of these is an imperative sentence?

   Ⓐ When will you return?   Ⓒ The lights glow.

   🅑 Close the door, please.   Ⓓ none of the above

5. Which sentence has a mistake in punctuation?

   Ⓐ The picnic starts in a few hours.

   Ⓑ Hurry, or we will be late!

   🅒 How will David get to the lake.

   Ⓓ none of the above

Wolf Island (continued)

Analyzing the Selection

Read the questions below. Write complete sentences for your answer. Support your answer with information from the selections.

How is "Wolf Island" similar to "One Small Place in a Tree"? How is it different?

_____

_____

_____

_____

_____

_____

_____

_____

_____

_____

_____

Wolf Island (continued)

Oral Fluency Assessment

The Cloud Artist

"Look!" said Uncle Chuck. "Skywriting!" He pointed up into the blue sky.

Todd was spending the day in New York City with his favorite uncle. It was a Saturday in February, and they were seeing the sights. The two felt like ants surrounded by such tall buildings.

"I read about this in the newspaper," said Uncle Chuck. "For the next couple of days, an airplane will be creating cloud shapes in the sky."

"Wow," said Todd. He watched as the outline of the cloud started to fade. Uncle Chuck grabbed Todd's hand and began racing from corner to corner. He started peering up and down the crowded streets.

"What are you looking for?" asked Todd.

"The cloud artist," Uncle Chuck explained, "he's down here somewhere."

Todd was puzzled. "You mean the artist isn't the pilot of the plane?" he asked.

Uncle Chuck shook his head. "No, his name is Tad Muniz. He takes photographs of things. He designed the clouds the plane is making." Uncle Chuck paused. "He sounds like an interesting artist. Maybe we can find a place that is showing his work."

1–9	
10–12	
13–23	
24–34	
35–45	
46–47	
48–58	
59–69	
70–73	
74–84	
85–94	
95–105	
106–108	
109–115	
116–124	
125	
126–137	
138–140	
141–152	
153–162	
163–172	
173–184	

EVALUATING CODES FOR ORAL FLUENCY

sky (/) words read incorrectly

blue
^ sky (^) inserted word
( ]) after the last word

READING RATE AND ACCURACY

Total Words Read: _____

Number of Errors: _____

Number of Correct Words Read Per Minute (WPM): _____

Accuracy Rate: _____

(Number of Correct Words Read per Minute ÷ Total Words Read)

READING FLUENCY

	Low	Average	High
Decoding ability	○	○	○
Pace	○	○	○
Syntax	○	○	○
Self-correction	○	○	○
Intonation	○	○	○

Record student rates on the Oral Fluency Scores pages.

Name _____ Date _____ Score _____

Two Days in May

Vocabulary

Read each item. Fill in the bubble for the answer you think is correct.

1. Which homophone pair best completes this sentence?

Put _____ toys over _____.

Ⓐ our/hour

Ⓒ your/you're

Ⓑ their/there

Ⓓ ate/eight

2. Another word for **relocates** is

Ⓐ loses.

Ⓒ moves.

Ⓑ chases.

Ⓓ bends.

3. A deer has **sharp** hearing. This means its hearing

Ⓐ is very good.

Ⓑ is affected by its antlers.

Ⓒ can be dangerous.

Ⓓ may not always be good.

4. The deer were **stranded** in the yard. **Stranded** means

Ⓐ standing.

Ⓒ sniffing the air.

Ⓑ left helpless.

Ⓓ getting worried.

5. The deer slept **cautiously.** This means the deer slept

Ⓐ making snoring noises.

Ⓑ curled up in a ball.

Ⓒ gathered close together.

Ⓓ with close care.

Two Days in May (continued)

Comprehension

Read the following questions carefully. Then completely fill in the bubble of each correct answer. You may look back at the selection to find the answer to each of the questions.

1. The deer could not stay in the city. Why not?

    Ⓐ There was not enough food.

    🅑 The city was not a safe place.

    Ⓒ People wanted them for pets.

    Ⓓ It was too noisy in the city.

2. Why do deer sometimes wander into cities?

    Ⓐ The new roads make it easy.

    Ⓑ The cities seem interesting.

    🅒 The forests are disappearing.

    Ⓓ The city people are nice to them.

Two Days in May (continued)

3. Deer coming into a city is most like

Ⓐ a child getting lost in a park.

Ⓑ a bird building a nest in a tree.

Ⓒ a fish swimming in a stream.

Ⓓ a cow eating grass in a field.

4. Which of these best describes the Pigeon Lady?

Ⓐ an animal control officer

Ⓑ a little bit silly

Ⓒ a nosy person

Ⓓ an animal lover

5. What Sonia and the other people did shows that

Ⓐ they liked the country better than the city.

Ⓑ they thought the deer would find their own way home.

Ⓒ they really cared about the deer.

Ⓓ they wanted the deer out of the garden.

Two Days in May (continued)

Read the following questions carefully. Use complete sentences to answer the questions. Possible answers below

6. How do the neighbors protect the deer from the animal control officer?

   The neighbors stand around the deer until the wildlife rescuer arrives.

7. Which words tell about the city's sounds in this selection?

   The words are *rumbling, honking, beeping, humming,* and *buzzing.*

8. How do the deer seem to feel about the crowd of people?

   The deer are alert and careful, but they are not very afraid.

9. Where does Carl Jackson take the deer?

   Carl Jackson takes the deer to the woods outside of the city.

10. How do the neighbors pass the time while they wait?

   They get to know each other better and share what they know about deer.

Two Days in May (continued)

Read the question below. Write complete sentences for your answer. Support your answer with information from the selection.

Linking to the Concepts What lessons does this selection teach about working together?

_____

_____

_____

_____

_____

Read the questions below. Your answer should be based on your own experience. Write complete sentences for your answer.

Personal Response What would you do if you found a wild animal that needed to be rescued? How did the selection affect your answer?

_____

_____

_____

_____

_____

Two Days in May (continued)

Grammar, Usage, and Mechanics

Read each question. Fill in the bubble beside the answer in each group that is correct. If none of the answers is correct, choose the last answer, "none of the above."

1. In which sentence is the subject underlined?

Ⓐ A ferry took <u>people</u> across the river.

🅑 A <u>ferry</u> took people across the river.

Ⓒ A ferry took people across the <u>river</u>.

Ⓓ none of the above

2. In which sentence is the object of the verb underlined?

🅐 Each person brought a <u>snack</u> to the party.

Ⓑ Each <u>person</u> brought a snack to the party.

Ⓒ Each person <u>brought</u> a snack to the party.

Ⓓ none of the above

3. Which sentence contains an object pronoun?

🅐 The store sold them.   Ⓒ They walked to the zoo.

Ⓑ My watch is a gift.   Ⓓ none of the above

4. Which sentence contains an object pronoun?

Ⓐ He caught the ball.   Ⓒ It ate the treat.

🅑 Angela found it.   Ⓓ none of the above

5. In which sentence is the subject underlined?

Ⓐ We <u>went</u> skiing in Colorado with them.

Ⓑ We went skiing in Colorado with <u>them</u>.

Ⓒ We went skiing <u>in</u> Colorado with them.

🅓 none of the above

Two Days in May (continued)

Analyzing the Selection

Read the question below. Write complete sentences for your answer. Support your answer with information from the selection.

If deer wandered into a city, do you think a group of neighbors would help them? Use information from the selection and your opinion to write your answer.

_____

_____

_____

_____

_____

_____

_____

_____

_____

_____

_____

_____

_____

Two Days in May (continued)

Oral Fluency Assessment

A Free Ride

Alice the bus driver saw six people and a floppy-eared dog	1–12
at her next stop. She slowed the bus down and opened the	13–24
door. The passengers got on, followed by the dog.	25–33
The dog sat down beside a woman who had gotten on board.	34–45
He wagged his tail as passengers came and went. He was	46–56
having a wonderful time.	57–60
At one of the stops, the woman next to the dog got up to leave.	61–75
"Don't forget your dog!" Alice called.	76–81
To her surprise, the dog did not belong to the woman. Alice	82–93
made a radio call to her boss and learned that the dog's owner	94–106
had seen the dog get on board but had not been able to catch	107–120
up before the bus left.	121–125
Meanwhile, the dog was enjoying himself. Everyone who	126–133
saw him smiled and gave him a pat.	134–141
Alice drove back to the stop where the dog had boarded.	142–152
A man rushed to greet them.	153–158
"I am so sorry!" he said. "Max loves to ride in cars, and he	159–172
must have wanted to do a little sightseeing."	173–180
"He was a good passenger," said Alice with a smile.	181–190

EVALUATING CODES FOR ORAL FLUENCY

sky   (/) words read incorrectly

blue

^ sky   (^) inserted word

( ) after the last word

READING RATE AND ACCURACY

Total Words Read: _____

Number of Errors: _____

Number of Correct Words
Read Per Minute (WPM): _____

Accuracy Rate: _____

(Number of Correct Words Read per
Minute ÷ Total Words Read)

READING FLUENCY

	Low	Average	High
Decoding ability	○	○	○
Pace	○	○	○
Syntax	○	○	○
Self-correction	○	○	○
Intonation	○	○	○

Record student rates on the Oral Fluency Scores pages.

Name _____ Date _____ Score _____

Crinkleroot's Guide to Knowing Animal Habitats

Vocabulary

Read each item. Fill in the bubble for the answer you think is correct.

1. Vast is another word for very

    Ⓐ large.   Ⓒ private.

    Ⓑ little.   Ⓓ fast.

2. An example of an irregular plural is

    Ⓐ minutes.   Ⓒ oxen.

    Ⓑ cases.   Ⓓ knights.

3. Migrating animals are animals that are

    Ⓐ eating different plants.

    Ⓑ moving from place to place.

    Ⓒ chasing other animals for food.

    Ⓓ losing their winter fur.

4. Every habitat has a **variety** of animals. **Variety** means

    Ⓐ very few types of animals.

    Ⓑ many large animals.

    Ⓒ mostly water animals.

    Ⓓ many different types of animals.

5. Owls fly overhead looking for **prey.** What is **prey?**

    Ⓐ twigs and leaves   Ⓒ streams for water

    Ⓑ animals to eat   Ⓓ places to nest

Crinkleroot's Guide to Knowing Animal Habitats (continued)

Comprehension

**Read the following questions carefully. Then
completely fill in the bubble of each correct answer.
You may look back at the selection to find the answer
to each of the questions.**

1. This selection is told from the

    Ⓐ third-person point of view of a woodland animal.

    Ⓑ second-person point of view.

    Ⓒ third-person point of view of the grandmother.

    Ⓓ first-person point of view of a nature explorer.

2. Wildlife need all of these to live EXCEPT

    Ⓐ food.

    Ⓑ water.

    Ⓒ wind.

    Ⓓ hiding places.

Crinkleroot's Guide to Knowing Animal Habitats (continued)

3. A wetland is any place where water

   Ⓐ is near the top of the ground.

   Ⓑ dries up in a very short while.

   Ⓒ flows very quickly.

   Ⓓ is difficult to find.

4. Why are woodland animals sometimes hard to see?

   Ⓐ There are not very many of them.

   Ⓑ They can be hidden by the trees.

   Ⓒ They only come out at night.

   Ⓓ They all live high in treetops.

5. Which of these habitats has the most types of insects and spiders?

   Ⓐ cornfields

   Ⓑ wetlands

   Ⓒ grasslands

   Ⓓ woodlands

Crinkleroot's Guide to Knowing Animal Habitats (continued)

Read the following questions carefully. Use complete sentences to answer the questions. Possible answers below

6. How are marshes different from swamps and bogs?

   <u>They have the most land and the least water; grasses and reeds grow there.</u>

7. What animals feed along roadsides in the daytime?

   <u>Rabbits, deer, woodchucks, crows, hawks, and kestrels feed there then.</u>

8. What animals feed in cornfields during the spring?

   <u>Gulls, swallows, and bluebirds eat there in spring.</u>

9. What are grasslands?

   <u>Grasslands are open spaces filled with grasses where wildlife can thrive.</u>

10. Where do animals find shade in the drylands?

   <u>They find it behind shrubs or cactus, under ledges, or with sand cover.</u>

Crinkleroot's Guide to Knowing Animal Habitats (continued)

Read the question below. Write complete sentences for your answer. Support your answer with information from the selection.

Linking to the Concepts Why do different types of animals live in different habitats?

_____

_____

_____

_____

_____

_____

Read the question below. Your answer should be based on your own experience. Write complete sentences for your answer.

Personal Response Which habitat do you think is most interesting? Explain your answer.

_____

_____

_____

_____

_____

Crinkleroot's Guide to Knowing Animal Habitats (continued)

Grammar, Usage, and Mechanics

Read each sentence. Fill in the bubble beside the pronoun in each answer group that can replace the underlined part in the sentence. If none of the answers is correct, choose the last answer, "none of the above."

1. Rob and Ben are taking art classes.

  Ⓐ Them   ● They

  Ⓑ He   Ⓓ none of the above

2. My sister gave me a book about science.

  Ⓐ It   Ⓒ Her

  ● She   Ⓓ none of the above

3. Ms. Howard walks her dog in the morning.

  Ⓐ I   Ⓒ They

  Ⓑ You   ● none of the above

4. Carol and I washed the dog.

  ● We

  Ⓑ It

  Ⓒ Us

  Ⓓ none of the above

5. Robert went to the mall with his friends.

  Ⓐ It

  Ⓑ Them

  ● He

  Ⓓ none of the above

Crinkleroot's Guide to Knowing Animal Habitats (continued)

Analyzing the Selection

Read the question below. Write complete sentences for your answer. Support your answer with information from the selections.

In this selection and other selections in the unit, you read about the relationship between plants and animals. Why are these relationships so important to all living things?

_____

_____

_____

_____

_____

_____

_____

_____

_____

_____

_____

_____

_____

Crinkleroot's Guide to Knowing Animal Habitats (continued)

Oral Fluency Assessment

Flying Spiders

Nature is filled with strange plants and animals. Some live in	1–11
far-off places. Others can be found right near your home. One	12–23
example is a special group of spiders.	24–30
Even though they do not have wings, these spiders can fly	31–41
though the air. They do this in an unusual way. The spiders	42–53
spin silk webs and use them like kites. They can do this	54–65
because a spider's web is very light and very strong. A web can	66–78
also be shaped in different ways.	79–84
The spider climbs to the top of a plant. It starts spinning	85–96
lines of silk. These silk lines seem to float in the air like sails.	97–110
The wind catches the lines and carries the spider away.	111–120
The spider cannot really steer through the air. It just lets the	121–133
wind carry it wherever. Spiders can travel miles on their kites	134–144
carried by the wind. After a while, the wind stops or the web	145–157
gets tangled in something. The spider climbs away from the	158–167
web and looks for a new home.	168–174

EVALUATING CODES FOR ORAL FLUENCY

sky   (/) words read incorrectly

blue
^   sky   (^) inserted word
           ( ]) after the last word

READING RATE AND ACCURACY

Total Words Read: _____

Number of Errors: _____

Number of Correct Words
Read Per Minute (WPM): _____

Accuracy Rate: _____

(Number of Correct Words Read per
Minute ÷ Total Words Read)

READING FLUENCY

	Low	Average	High
Decoding ability	○	○	○
Pace	○	○	○
Syntax	○	○	○
Self-correction	○	○	○
Intonation	○	○	○

Record student rates on the Oral Fluency Scores pages.

Name _____ Date _____ Score _____

Expository Writing

Writing Situation
An unusual animal or habitat

Audience
Your friends

Directions for Writing
You have learned about unusual animals and their habitats, the places where animals live. Choose an unusual animal or a habitat you find interesting. Describe the animal or habitat in a way that will be interesting to the reader.

Checklist
You will earn the best score if you

- think about your animal or habitat before you start writing.
- write in a way that is interesting to your readers.
- begin telling about the animal or habitat in the first paragraph.
- use describing words to tell about the animal or habitat.
- use action words to show what the animal does.
- give many interesting details about the animal or habitat.
- use subjects, verbs, and modifiers correctly.
- write complete sentences and avoid fragments or run-ons.
- choose words that mean what you want to say.
- read your writing after you finish and check for mistakes.

UNIT 2 — Four Point Rubrics for Expository Writing

Genre	1 Point	2 Points	3 Points	4 Points
Expository	Composition has no introduction or clear topic. It offers a group of loosely related facts or a series of poorly written steps. No conclusion is included.	Composition is clearly organized around main points with supportive facts or assertions. Composition has no clear introduction, but its topic is identifiable. However, it includes many facts unrelated to the topic, or it describes things in a disorganized way. No conclusion is included.	Main points and supportive details can be identified, but they are not clearly marked. Composition has an introduction and offers facts about the topic. Some facts may be irrelevant, or some ideas may be vague or out of order. The report is fairly well organized but doesn't have a strong conclusion.	Traces and constructs a line of argument, identifying part-to-whole relations. Main points are supported with logical and appropriate evidence. Composition begins with an introduction and offers relevant facts about the topic or describes the topic appropriately. The report is organized using cause/effect, comparison/contrast, or another pattern. It ends with a strong conclusion.

Writing Traits	1 Point	2 Points	3 Points	4 Points
Focus	Topic is unclear or wanders and must be inferred. Extraneous material may be present.	Topic/position/direction is unclear and must be inferred.	Topic/position is stated and direction/purpose is previewed and maintained. Mainly stays on topic.	Topic/position is clearly stated, previewed, and maintained throughout the paper. Topics and details are tied together with a central theme or purpose that is maintained/threaded throughout the paper.
Ideas/Content	Superficial and/or minimal content is included.	Main ideas are understandable, although they may be overly broad or simplistic, and the results may not be effective. Supporting detail is limited, insubstantial, overly general or off topic.	The writing is clear and focused. The reader can easily understand the main ideas. Support is present, although it may be limited or rather general.	Writing is exceptionally clear, focused, and interesting. Main ideas stand out and are developed by strong support and rich details.
Elaboration (supporting details and examples that develop the main idea)	States ideas or points with minimal detail to support them.	Includes sketchy, redundant, or general details; some may be irrelevant. Support for key ideas is very uneven.	Includes mix of general statements and specific details/examples. Support is mostly relevant but may be uneven and lack depth in places.	Includes specific details and supporting examples for each key point/idea. May use compare/contrast to support.

Writing Conventions	1 Point	2 Points	3 Points	4 Points
Conventions Overall	Numerous errors in usage, grammar, spelling, capitalization, and punctuation repeatedly distract the reader and make the text difficult to read. The reader finds it difficult to focus on the message.	The writing demonstrates limited control of standard writing conventions (punctuation, spelling, capitalization, grammar, and usage). Errors sometimes impede readability.	The writing demonstrates control of standard writing conventions (punctuation, spelling, capitalization, grammar, and usage). Minor errors, while perhaps noticeable, do not impede readability.	The writing demonstrates exceptionally strong control of standard writing conventions (punctuation, spelling, capitalization, grammar, and usage) and uses them effectively to enhance communication. Errors are so few and so minor that the reader can easily skim over them.

Name _____ Date _____ Score _____

It's a Deal!

Vocabulary

Read each item. Fill in the bubble for the answer you think is correct.

1. **Ancient** means

   Ⓐ young.   Ⓒ very old.

   Ⓑ fast.   Ⓓ too small.

2. A **deal** is a(n)

   Ⓐ agreement.   Ⓒ enemy.

   Ⓑ friend.   Ⓓ book.

3. Long ago, **valuable** metals were traded. **Valuable** means

   Ⓐ very heavy.   Ⓒ worth a lot of money.

   Ⓑ useless.   Ⓓ natural.

4. Lydia was a **kingdom**. A **kingdom** is a

   Ⓐ place ruled by a king or queen.

   Ⓑ desert with a few cities.

   Ⓒ town with its own money.

   Ⓓ group of traders or merchants.

5. Metal was hard to carry around, so a better **solution** was found—paper money. A **solution** is

   Ⓐ a way to get richer.

   Ⓑ an organized group.

   Ⓒ a way to carry things easily.

   Ⓓ an answer to a problem.

It's a Deal! (continued)

Comprehension

Read the following questions carefully. Then completely fill in the bubble of each correct answer. You may look back at the selection to find the answer to each of the questions.

1. When people used metal to buy things, they had to

   Ⓐ melt down the metal each time they paid.

   Ⓑ have their metal made into jewelry first.

   Ⓒ cut the bars into small pieces to pay.

   Ⓓ weigh the pieces every time they paid.

2. What type of money did people in Lydia use?

   Ⓐ cow horns

   Ⓑ metal stamped with a lion's head

   Ⓒ paper money

   Ⓓ wooden coins with a bear's head

It's a Deal! (continued)

3. Why did people change from metal to paper money?

Ⓐ All the metal was used up.

Ⓑ No one trusted metal any more.

Ⓒ Metal was too hard to carry and use.

Ⓓ Only a few countries had enough metal.

4. The earliest kind of paper money was

Ⓐ a note that promised people had coins at home.

Ⓑ an ancient scroll that showed what people owed.

Ⓒ small sheets of paper from the kings of Lydia.

Ⓓ a painting showing what people had to trade.

5. The author wrote this selection in order to

Ⓐ explain why metal bars were too heavy to carry around as money.

Ⓑ tell why people thought the kings of Lydia were honest.

Ⓒ show how people moved from bartering to using paper money.

Ⓓ persuade readers why bartering is the best way to do business.

It's a Deal! (continued)

Read the following questions carefully. Use complete sentences to answer the questions. Possible answers below

6. What does it mean to barter?

Bartering is trading one thing for another without using money.

7. What was one of the problems with bartering?

If no one wanted what you had, you could not get what you needed.

8. What were some early types of money before metal?

Early types of money included cows, butter, corn, shells, and salt.

9. Why did people trust money in Lydia?

It was stamped with the king's mark, and the kings were known to be honest.

10. How is paper money today different than when it was first used?

Today's paper money does not reflect the coins a person has at home.

It's a Deal! (continued)

Read the question below. Write complete sentences for your answer. Support your answer with information from the selection.

Linking to the Concepts How is using money better than bartering?

_____

_____

_____

_____

_____

Read the questions below. Your answer should be based on your own experience. Write complete sentences for your answer.

Personal Response Write about a time you made a trade or someone you know made a trade. What was traded? How did it work out?

_____

_____

_____

_____

_____

It's a Deal! (continued)

Grammar, Usage, and Mechanics

In items 1–3, fill in the bubble beside the answer in each group that is the best way to combine the two sentences. In items 4 and 5, fill in the bubble that identifies the two simple sentences in the compound sentence.

1. A castle was nearby. We did not visit it.

Ⓐ A castle was nearby, but we did not visit it.

Ⓑ We visited a castle nearby.

Ⓒ Nearby, we did not visit a castle.

2. Luke climbed. Kate looked for fossils.

Ⓐ Climbing, Luke and Kate looked for fossils.

Ⓑ Luke climbed looking for fossils.

Ⓒ Kate looked for fossils, and Luke climbed.

3. Carol walks home. Jill meets her on the way.

Ⓐ Jill walking home meets Carol on the way.

Ⓑ Carol walks home, and Jill meets her on the way.

Ⓒ Carol and Jill walk home, on the way meeting.

4. Rick was in the parade, so his mother cheered.

Ⓐ Rick was in. The parade so his mother cheered.

Ⓑ Rick cheered. His mother was in the parade.

Ⓒ Rick was in the parade. His mother cheered.

5. Trees lined the road, and each house had a garden.

Ⓐ Trees lined the road. Each house had a garden.

Ⓑ Each house lined. Trees were in a garden.

Ⓒ Trees lined. The road had a garden.

It's a Deal! (continued)

Analyzing the Selection

Read the questions below. Write complete sentences for your response. Support your answer with information from the selection.

Do you think that it is important today that people use money rather than bartering? Why or why not?

_____

_____

_____

_____

_____

_____

_____

_____

_____

_____

_____

_____

It's a Deal! (continued)

Oral Fluency Assessment

Worm Patrol

Abe looked out the window. The rain had stopped, but the sky was still gray. He glanced over at his mom and said, "I think it's time to go gardening."

"Very funny, Abe," his mother said. "Look at the weather outside!"

Abe tried not to smile as he said, "Well, there is no garden yet, but there is a lot to do to get it ready." He went into the kitchen and grabbed a plastic bowl next to the sink. The bowl was full of fruit scraps, bread crusts, and eggshells. Abe and his mother went into the yard. Abe went up to a brown bin and lifted its lid. Inside were grass clippings, banana peels, and coffee grounds.

His mother took a stick and pushed back some of the compost. Underneath were all sorts of wriggling red worms.

"Wow," she said, "I can't believe how many worms there are!"

"Maybe we should have shirts printed up that say *Worm Patrol*," Abe replied. "In the spring, we can move the worms to our new garden."

1–11
12–23
24–30
31–40
41
42–54
55–70
71–82
83–93
94–107
108–117
118–119
120–130
131–139
140–150
151–160
161–171
172–175

**EVALUATING CODES
FOR ORAL FLUENCY**

sky   (/) words read incorrectly

blue
^   sky   (^) inserted word

          ( ]) after the last word

READING RATE AND ACCURACY

Total Words Read: _____

Number of Errors: _____

Number of Correct Words
Read Per Minute (WPM):   _____

Accuracy Rate: _____

(Number of Correct Words Read per
Minute ÷ Total Words Read)

READING FLUENCY

	Low	Average	High
Decoding ability	○	○	○
Pace	○	○	○
Syntax	○	○	○
Self-correction	○	○	○
Intonation	○	○	○

Record student rates on the Oral Fluency Scores pages.

Name _____ Date _____ Score _____

The Go-Around Dollar

Vocabulary

Read each item. Fill in the bubble for the answer you think is correct.

1. Adding the inflectional ending **-ed** to base verbs creates

  Ⓐ compound words.   ● the past tense.

  Ⓑ the present tense.   Ⓓ the future tense.

2. Something that is **counterfeit** is

  ● fake.   Ⓒ heavy.

  Ⓑ expensive.   Ⓓ cheap.

3. The bald eagle is our national **emblem.** An **emblem** is

  Ⓐ a place where money is made.

  Ⓑ a bird that hunts animals for its food.

  Ⓒ a type of money.

  ● a sign that stands for something.

4. Someone must **inspect** money when it is damaged. **Inspect** means

  ● to look at closely.   Ⓒ to share.

  Ⓑ to fix or repair.   Ⓓ to send away.

5. Money is used to pay **debts.** What are **debts?**

  Ⓐ buildings

  ● things that are owed

  Ⓒ different types of food

  Ⓓ workers

The Go-Around Dollar (continued)

Comprehension

Read the following questions carefully. Then completely fill in the bubble of each correct answer. You may look back at the selection to find the answer to each of the questions.

1. Which of these happened first in the selection?

Ⓐ Kathy walked Biscuit.

Ⓑ Jennifer got a dollar as part of her change.

Ⓒ Matt and Eric found a dollar.

Ⓓ Rob asked Kathy for help.

2. Worn out dollar bills are

Ⓐ torn and put into frames.

Ⓑ stored in a big building.

Ⓒ washed and used again.

Ⓓ shredded into small pieces.

The Go-Around Dollar (continued)

3. Water does not hurt a dollar bill because dollar bills

Ⓐ are made with strong paper.

Ⓑ weigh very little.

Ⓒ have two kinds of ink.

Ⓓ are made the same size.

4. This selection is mostly about

Ⓐ where dollar bills are made.

Ⓑ the life of a dollar bill.

Ⓒ why the dollar bill is green.

Ⓓ what you can buy with a dollar.

5. Who had the dollar bill just before Kathy?

Ⓐ Rob

Ⓑ Jennifer

Ⓒ Matt

Ⓓ Eric

The Go-Around Dollar (continued)

Read the following questions carefully. Use complete sentences to answer the questions. Possible answers below

6. Why do store owners sometimes put a dollar bill inside a frame?

   They frame their first dollar to remember it because it is special.

7. Why did the ticket seller make a phone call?

   The ticket seller called because he thought the dollar looked strange.

8. Why is the formula for the dollar bill's ink a secret?

   The formula is a secret to prevent people from making fake money.

9. What is the reason for a serial number on a dollar bill?

   It tells people the dollar bill is real and makes it harder to create fake money.

10. When does money go to Federal Reserve Banks?

   It goes after it has been cut from sheets and stacked into "bricks."

The Go-Around Dollar (continued)

Read the question below. Write complete sentences for your answer. Support your answer with information from the selection.

Linking to the Concepts How is the dollar bill a useful part of everyday life?

_____

_____

_____

_____

_____

Read the questions below. Your answer should be based on your own experience. Write complete sentences for your answer.

Personal Response If you got the dollar bill in this selection, how would you probably spend it? Why would you spend it this way?

_____

_____

_____

_____

_____

The Go-Around Dollar (continued)

Grammar, Usage, and Mechanics

Read each question. Fill in the bubble beside the answer in each group that is correct. If none of the answers is correct, choose the last answer, "none of the above."

1. In which sentence is the adjective underlined?

Ⓐ A deer with huge antlers walked <u>across</u> the path.

Ⓑ A deer with huge antlers <u>walked</u> across the path.

Ⓒ A deer with <u>huge</u> antlers walked across the path.

Ⓓ none of the above

2. In which sentence is the adjective underlined?

Ⓐ <u>Wear</u> the red raincoat.

Ⓒ Wear the red <u>raincoat</u>.

Ⓑ Wear the <u>red</u> raincoat.

Ⓓ none of the above

3. In which sentence is the adjective underlined?

Ⓐ They heard a loud <u>noise</u>.

Ⓒ <u>They</u> heard a loud noise.

Ⓑ They <u>heard</u> a loud noise.

Ⓓ none of the above

4. In which sentence is the adjective used correctly?

Ⓐ The basement is the damper room in the house.

Ⓑ The basement is the damperest room in the house.

Ⓒ The basement is the dampest room in the house.

Ⓓ none of the above

5. In which sentence is the adjective used correctly?

Ⓐ This tent is roomest than the other one.

Ⓑ This tent is roomier than the other one.

Ⓒ This tent is more roomier than the other one.

Ⓓ none of the above

The Go-Around Dollar (continued)

Analyzing the Selection

Read the questions below. Write complete sentences for your answer. Support your answer with information from the selections.

Why is it so important to protect money so that people know it is real? What might happen if lots of fake money were used?

_____

_____

_____

_____

_____

_____

_____

_____

_____

_____

_____

The Go-Around Dollar (continued)

Oral Fluency Assessment

Snake Story

Snakes are members of the reptile family. They have dry, 1–10
scaly skin. They are cold-blooded animals. This means they 11–20
must stay in the sun to keep warm. If it is too hot, they need 21–35
to find shade where they can cool down. They cannot control 36–46
their own body temperature. 47–50

As they grow, snakes shed their skin. The old skin comes 51–61
off, and there is a new skin underneath. Each time a snake 62–73
sheds, its new skin is a little larger than before. 74–83

There are many different kinds of snakes. Some are small 84–93
and may be only a few inches long. Others are huge, as long 94–106
as thirty feet. 107–109

Snakes do not have legs, but they can move very quickly 110–120
along the ground. When they have to catch food, they seem to 121–132
move like lightning. 133–135

Snakes are meat eaters. They swallow their food whole, and 136–145
after a snake has eaten, there is a bulge in its body. The bulge 146–159
moves down as the snake digests its food. 160–167

**EVALUATING CODES
FOR ORAL FLUENCY**

sky   (/) words read incorrectly

blue
^   sky   (^) inserted word
        ( ]) after the last word

READING RATE AND ACCURACY

Total Words Read: _____

Number of Errors: _____

Number of Correct Words
Read Per Minute (WPM):   _____

Accuracy Rate: _____

(Number of Correct Words Read per
Minute ÷ Total Words Read)

READING FLUENCY

	Low	Average	High
Decoding ability	○	○	○
Pace	○	○	○
Syntax	○	○	○
Self-correction	○	○	○
Intonation	○	○	○

Record student rates on the Oral Fluency Scores pages.

Name _____ Date _____ Score _____

Lemons and Lemonade

Vocabulary

Read each item. Fill in the bubble for the answer you think is correct.

1. A **stack** is a

Ⓐ treat.   Ⓒ trap.

🅑 pile.   Ⓓ plan.

2. What is the superlative form of the adjective *cool?*

Ⓐ coolester   🅒 coolest

Ⓑ most cooler   Ⓓ coolerest

3. At first, Karly's **expenses** were low. **Expenses** means the

🅐 money spent to buy or make things.

Ⓑ people who want to buy things.

Ⓒ money made by selling things.

Ⓓ number of things put up for sale.

4. Karly made a **profit.** What is **profit?**

Ⓐ things needed to make a product

Ⓑ a small stand to sell things

Ⓒ a person who starts his or her own business

🅓 money left after everything has been paid for

5. There was a **demand** for lemonade. A **demand** means

Ⓐ a stand.   🅒 a desire for a product.

Ⓑ nice weather.   Ⓓ enough time.

Lemons and Lemonade (continued)

Comprehension

Read the following questions carefully. Then completely fill in the bubble of each correct answer. You may look back at the selection to find the answer to each of the questions.

1. Which of these would not happen in real life?

- (A) Karly sets up a lemonade stand near her house.
- (B) Karly's mother helps her set up the stand.
- (C) Karly makes lemonade for everyone in the world.
- (D) Karly makes a sign from cardboard for her stand.

2. Who is Karly's first customer?

- (A) Mr. Smith
- (B) Mrs. Crane
- (C) Josh
- (D) Shaun

Lemons and Lemonade (continued)

3. Which of these are the two key factors in setting prices?

Ⓐ supply and demand

Ⓑ profit and capital

Ⓒ gross and net profit

Ⓓ customers and partners

4. Karly's mother says Karly does not have a monopoly because

Ⓐ her mother does not want her to daydream.

Ⓑ Josh and Shaun also have a lemonade stand.

Ⓒ Karly does not make enough money to buy supplies.

Ⓓ her mother gives her fruit snacks to sell.

5. Which of these sentences from the selection is an opinion?

Ⓐ I'll be rich!

Ⓑ All of your supplies are called capital.

Ⓒ There's a softball game going on today.

Ⓓ That night, Karly made a new sign.

Lemons and Lemonade (continued)

Read the following questions carefully. Use complete sentences to answer the questions. Possible answers below

6. What are the two kinds of things businesses might sell?

Some businesses sell goods, while others sell services.

7. What is the difference between gross and net profit?

Gross profit: all the money taken in; net profit: money left after paying bills.

8. How does Karly test the market?

She raises her price to see how much people would pay for the lemonade.

9. What does Karly do when she has competition?

She lowers the lemonade price and expands by selling fruit snacks.

10. What do Josh and Shaun mean when they ask Karly to be their business partner?

They want to work together in the same business to sell lemonade.

UNIT 3 **Lesson 3**

Lemons and Lemonade (continued)

Read the question below. Write complete sentences for your answer. Support your answer with information from the selection.

Linking to the Concepts What did Karly learn by opening her own business?

_____

_____

_____

_____

Read the questions below. Your answer should be based on your own experience. Write complete sentences for your answer.

Personal Response What kind of business would you like to open? How would you get people to come to your business?

_____

_____

_____

_____

Lemons and Lemonade (continued)

Grammar, Usage, and Mechanics

Read each question. Fill in the bubble beside the answer in each group that is correct. If none of the answers is correct, choose the last answer, "none of the above."

1. Which sentence has correct punctuation?

Ⓐ A bird is in Mr Lee's yard. Ⓒ A bird is in Mr. lee's yard

Ⓑ A bird is in Mr. Lee's yard. Ⓓ none of the above

2. Which sentence has correct punctuation?

Ⓐ The playground on Morris St is closed.

Ⓑ The playground on Morris St is closed

Ⓒ The playground on Morris St. is closed.

Ⓓ none of the above

3. Which sentence has correct capitalization?

Ⓐ The last tennis match will be on may 14.

Ⓑ The last Tennis Match will be on May 14.

Ⓒ The last Tennis match will be on may 14.

Ⓓ none of the above

4. Which sentence is correct?

Ⓐ My sister goes to College in Denver, Colorado.

Ⓑ My sister goes to college in Denver, Colorado.

Ⓒ My sister goes to college in denver, Colorado

Ⓓ none of the above

5. Which sentence is correct?

Ⓐ Jane saw Dr. Gorrie. Ⓒ Jane saw Dr Gorrie.

Ⓑ Jane saw dr. Gorrie. Ⓓ none of the above

Lemons and Lemonade (continued)

Analyzing the Selection

Read the question below. Write complete sentences for your answer. Support your answer with information from the selections.

Think about what you have read so far in this unit. Why do people work so hard to get money? Use information from the selections, information you already know, and your opinion in your answer.

_____

_____

_____

_____

_____

_____

_____

_____

_____

_____

Lemons and Lemonade (continued)

Oral Fluency Assessment

New School

All the children in Anne's town had to go to a different school for the third grade. Anne was very afraid to go to a different school. She liked her old school and her teachers. She asked her mother if she could stay in second grade again.

"You must go with your class," her mother said. "Third grade will be lots of fun. You'll see."

Anne thought she would not have to go to school if she pretended she was sick. She told her mother she was too sick to go to school. Anne's mother knew that Anne was really more afraid than she was sick. She took Anne to school the first day. They walked into the new building together. She helped Anne find her class.

Her new teacher was smiling and shook hands with Anne's mother. The teacher said they were going to have a good third grade this year. Anne saw Mary and Ellen and Tommy from her old class. By the time Anne's mother left, she had forgotten about being afraid or sick.

1–12
13–25
26–35
36–47
48–58
59–65
66–77
78–89
90–101
102–114
115–124
125–127
128–137
138–149
150–160
161–172
173–177

EVALUATING CODES FOR ORAL FLUENCY

sky (/) words read incorrectly

blue
^ sky (^) inserted word
( ]) after the last word

READING RATE AND ACCURACY

Total Words Read: _____

Number of Errors: _____

Number of Correct Words Read Per Minute (WPM): _____

Accuracy Rate: _____

(Number of Correct Words Read per Minute ÷ Total Words Read)

READING FLUENCY

	Low	Average	High
Decoding ability	○	○	○
Pace	○	○	○
Syntax	○	○	○
Self-correction	○	○	○
Intonation	○	○	○

Record student rates on the Oral Fluency Scores pages.

Name _____ Date _____ Score _____

Madam C. J. Walker: Self-Made Millionaire

Vocabulary

Read each item. Fill in the bubble for the answer you think is correct.

1. What is the comparative form of the adjective *good?*

   good, _____, best

   (A) gooder   (C) bestest

   (B) goodest   (D) better ●

2. Hired means to give someone a(n)

   (A) idea.   (C) plan.

   (B) job. ●   (D) product.

3. Madam C. J. Walker became a **millionaire.** This means

   (A) she had a million dollars or more. ●

   (B) she had her own business.

   (C) she had many friends and salespeople.

   (D) she had her own factory.

4. She **charged** for hair care goods. **Charged** means she

   (A) gave them away.   (C) asked for money. ●

   (B) made people sell.   (D) gave people money.

5. Madam Walker **sued** the theater. **Sued** means she

   (A) worked hard to change unfair laws.

   (B) made a case against them in court. ●

   (C) listened to someone else's ideas.

   (D) started another business.

Madam C. J. Walker: Self-Made Millionaire (continued)

Comprehension

Read the following questions carefully. Then completely fill in the bubble of each correct answer. You may look back at the selection to find the answer to each of the questions.

1. When did Madam Walker go to school?

   Ⓐ when she was young

   Ⓑ after her daughter went to college

   Ⓒ when she worked on the cotton farm

   Ⓓ when she moved to Indianapolis

2. Madam Walker made hair products because

   Ⓐ she was losing her hair.

   Ⓑ she did not like washing clothes.

   Ⓒ she wanted to own a company.

   Ⓓ her daughter needed them.

Madam C. J. Walker: Self-Made Millionaire (continued)

3. A fact from the selection is that

   Ⓐ Madam Walker was a wonderful example for all women.

   Ⓑ Madam Walker hired lawyers to help manage the business.

   Ⓒ Madam Walker is the most important woman in history.

   Ⓓ segregation was the biggest problem in the country.

4. From which point of view is this selection written?

   Ⓐ from the first-person point of view of Madam Walker

   Ⓑ from the first-person point of view of A'Lelia

   Ⓒ from the second-person point of view

   Ⓓ from the third-person point of view

5. Which of these is an example of an opinion, not a fact?

   Ⓐ Madam Walker built a factory in Indiana.

   Ⓑ Madam Walker was a millionaire.

   Ⓒ Madam Walker worked harder than other businesswomen.

   Ⓓ A'Lelia moved to Harlem.

Madam C. J. Walker: Self-Made Millionaire (continued)

Read the following questions carefully. Use complete sentences to answer the questions. Possible answers below

6. Why did Madam Walker think African Americans needed to start businesses in their neighborhoods?

She thought this would create more jobs for African American workers.

7. How did Madam Walker use her money to help others?

She gave money to churches, schools, hospitals, and other causes.

8. What did Madam Walker do when a theater charged her more because she was African American?

First she sued the theater, then she built a theater for all to use.

9. How do you know this selection is realistic and not a fantasy?

It is not a fantasy because it is the biography of a real person.

10. How was A'Lelia like her mother?

She used her money to help people, and she died young like her mother.

Madam C. J. Walker: Self-Made Millionaire (continued)

Read the question below. Write complete sentences for your answer. Support your answer with information from the selection.

Linking to the Concepts How did Madam Walker become an example for other African American women?

_____

_____

_____

_____

_____

Read the question below. Your answer should be based on your own experience. Write complete sentences for your answer.

Personal Response If you were a millionaire, how would you use your money?

_____

_____

_____

_____

_____

Madam C. J. Walker: Self-Made Millionaire (continued)

Grammar, Usage, and Mechanics

Read each question. Fill in the bubble beside the answer in each group that is correct. If none of the answers is correct, choose the last answer, "none of the above."

1. Which sentence has correct article use?

Ⓐ Fran ate an orange. Ⓒ Give me an peach.

Ⓑ He owns a apple tree. Ⓓ none of the above

2. Which sentence has correct article use?

Ⓐ An cat ran up a oak. Ⓒ George saw a palm tree.

Ⓑ An willow tree is huge. Ⓓ none of the above

3. Which sentence has correct article use?

Ⓐ The blue jay picked up a acorn.

Ⓑ The picnic food was in an basket.

Ⓒ Do you have a extra pair of socks?

Ⓓ none of the above

4. Which sentence has a mistake?

Ⓐ Dad put grandfather's picture in a frame.

Ⓑ The bug was about a inch long.

Ⓒ The team had a meeting before the game.

Ⓓ none of the above

5. Which sentence has a mistake?

Ⓐ The goat walked along an narrow ledge.

Ⓑ Mom put a pitcher of water on the table.

Ⓒ An adjustable wrench is a useful tool.

Ⓓ none of the above

Madam C. J. Walker: Self-Made Millionaire (continued)

Analyzing the Selection

Read the question below. Write complete sentences for your answer. Support your answer with information from the selection.

In your opinion, why were Madam Walker's accomplishments important?

_____

_____

_____

_____

_____

_____

_____

_____

_____

_____

_____

_____

Madam C. J. Walker: Self-Made Millionaire (continued)

Oral Fluency Assessment

Vacation Surprise

It was the start of spring vacation, and Pam was talking to	1–11
her mom about all the things she wanted to do during the week.	12–24
Pam's mom just listened and smiled.	25–31
Just then, Pam's dad came in the door. Pam was surprised	32–42
because it was only noon, and usually her dad got home at	43–54
suppertime. "Hi, Dad," Pam said. "What are you doing home	55–64
so early?"	65–66
Pam's dad pulled some papers out of his coat pocket. He	67–77
had a strange grin on his face. "Well," he said, "I got to thinking	78–91
about your spring vacation, and I decided all of us could use	92–103
a little time off. How would you like to take a cruise along the	104–117
Mexican coast?"	118–119
Pam's eyes grew wider. She looked from her mom to her	120–130
dad. This was clearly something they had planned together.	131–139
Pam jumped up and gave each of her parents a hug. She looked	140–152
at the papers her dad had brought home.	153–160

**EVALUATING CODES
FOR ORAL FLUENCY**

sky   (/) words read incorrectly

blue

^   sky   (^) inserted word

( ]) after the last word

READING RATE AND ACCURACY

Total Words Read: _____

Number of Errors: _____

Number of Correct Words
Read Per Minute (WPM):   _____

Accuracy Rate: _____

(Number of Correct Words Read per
Minute ÷ Total Words Read)

READING FLUENCY

	Low	Average	High
Decoding ability	○	○	○
Pace	○	○	○
Syntax	○	○	○
Self-correction	○	○	○
Intonation	○	○	○

Record student rates on the Oral Fluency Scores pages.

Name _____ Date _____ Score _____

Uncle Jed's Barbershop

Vocabulary

Read each item. Fill in the bubble for the answer you think is correct.

1. **Unconscious** means

   Ⓐ dangerous.   Ⓒ not late.

   Ⓑ not awake.   Ⓓ foolish.

2. What is the superlative form of the adjective *many*?

   many, more, _____

   Ⓐ most   Ⓒ morest

   Ⓑ mostest   Ⓓ maniest

3. Uncle Jed wanted some fancy **equipment.** This means he wanted

   Ⓐ new customers.   Ⓒ tools and supplies.

   Ⓑ another shop.   Ⓓ new investors.

4. Mama **bundled** Sara Jean in the blanket. What does **bundled** mean in this sentence?

   Ⓐ noticed   Ⓒ carried

   Ⓑ flipped   Ⓓ wrapped

5. Uncle Jed lost money in a **failing** bank. A **failing** bank is a bank that is

   Ⓐ small and friendly.

   Ⓑ losing money.

   Ⓒ mostly for farmers.

   Ⓓ in the country.

Uncle Jed's Barbershop (continued)

Comprehension

Read the following questions carefully. Then completely fill in the bubble of each correct answer. You may look back at the selection to find the answer to each of the questions.

1. Which of these best describes Uncle Jed?

Ⓐ filled with foolish dreams

Ⓑ friendly but careless

Ⓒ hardworking and kind

Ⓓ always joking and having fun

2. Who is narrating this selection?

Ⓐ Sarah Jean

Ⓑ Uncle Jed

Ⓒ Sarah Jean's mama

Ⓓ Ernest Walters

Uncle Jed's Barbershop (continued)

3. Uncle Jed lost over three thousand dollars because

- Ⓐ people did not pay him.

- Ⓑ the money burned in a fire.

- Ⓒ someone stole it.

- **Ⓓ** a bank failed.

4. How did Uncle Jed teach Sarah Jean to dream?

- Ⓐ by having many customers

- Ⓑ by living a long time

- **Ⓒ** by achieving his own dream

- Ⓓ by saving money

5. From the selection, you know that

- Ⓐ Sarah Jean learned to cut hair.

- **Ⓑ** people respected Uncle Jed.

- Ⓒ Uncle Jed's shop is still around.

- Ⓓ the Great Depression was not so bad.

Uncle Jed's Barbershop (continued)

Read the following questions carefully. Use complete sentences to answer the questions. Possible answers below

6. Why does no one believe Uncle Jed will someday have his own shop?

People think it is an impossible dream, and Uncle Jed keeps having bad luck.

7. What did Uncle Jed do when his customers could not pay him?

He still cut their hair and let them share with him whatever they had.

8. Why does Uncle Jed work all night in his new shop?

He is so happy to have a shop that he does not want to stop cutting hair.

9. When does Sarah Jean first learn about Uncle Jed's dream?

She learns about it when she is a little girl and he tells her about it.

10. Why do so many people come to the opening of Uncle Jed's barbershop?

They come because they know how hard he has worked to reach his dream.

Uncle Jed's Barbershop (continued)

Read the question below. Write complete sentences for your answer. Support your answer with information from the selection.

Linking to the Concepts What does this selection say about being patient and working hard to make dreams come true?

_____

_____

_____

_____

_____

Read the questions below. Your answer should be based on your own experience. Write complete sentences for your answer.

Personal Response Write about a time when you wanted something very badly, but you had to wait for it. How long did you have to wait? Are you still waiting?

_____

_____

_____

_____

_____

Uncle Jed's Barbershop (continued)

Grammar, Usage, and Mechanics

Read each question. Fill in the bubble beside the answer in each group that is correct. If none of the answers is correct, choose the last answer, "none of the above."

1. Which sentence has a compound subject?

Ⓐ Mr. Hill had an idea.   Ⓒ Mary and her friends ran.

Ⓑ Mary liked Mr. Hill.   Ⓓ none of the above

2. Which sentence has a compound subject?

Ⓐ Sam and I left the park.   Ⓒ He ran and fell.

Ⓑ I went here and there.   Ⓓ none of the above

3. Which sentence has a compound predicate?

Ⓐ A group of bicycle riders passed by our house.

Ⓑ The riders went down the hill and turned the corner.

Ⓒ About an hour later, they came back up the hill.

Ⓓ none of the above

4. Which sentence has a compound predicate?

Ⓐ The car and truck drove the same speed.

Ⓑ The plane flew over fields and towns.

Ⓒ The red and silver train moved through the fields.

Ⓓ none of the above

5. What is the best way to combine these two sentences?

Jason tripped. He knocked the lamp over.

Ⓐ Jason tripped the lamp over.

Ⓑ Jason tripped and knocked the lamp over.

Ⓒ Jason tripped; knocked the lamp over.

Ⓓ none of the above

Uncle Jed's Barbershop (continued)

Analyzing the Selection

Read the questions below. Write complete sentences for your answer. Support your answer with information from the selections.

In this unit, you read about some people who were very successful. How do you define success? What part does money play in your definition?

_____

_____

_____

_____

_____

_____

_____

_____

_____

_____

_____

_____

Uncle Jed's Barbershop (continued)

Oral Fluency Assessment

A New Bill

Bill was a good boy, but he was very spoiled. If he did   1–13
not get his own way, he would get angry. The other children   14–25
grew tired of Bill's tantrums. They chose others to be their   26–36
playmates.   37

One day his parents decided a change was needed. Bill had   38–48
to behave at home and at school. Bill was very unhappy.   49–59

Nothing was working the way it had before. Bill decided   60–69
to go outside for a walk. The night was dark. Scary shadows   70–81
were everywhere. Bill ran from a big, barking dog. A car went   82–93
around the corner very fast and drove up on the sidewalk   94–104
near Bill. Then it began to rain. The wind blew. He was cold   105–117
and scared.   118–119

Bill ran all the way home. He said goodnight to his parents,   120–131
crawled into his warm bed, and fell asleep. The next morning,   132–142
when his mother came in to wake him, Bill smiled and hugged   143–154
her. He got up without complaining. He ate breakfast and   155–164
left for school smiling. From that day onward, Bill was a new   165–176
person. He finally realized how good his life was.   177–185

**EVALUATING CODES
FOR ORAL FLUENCY**

sky   (/) words read incorrectly

blue
^   sky   (^) inserted word
          ( ]) after the last word

READING RATE AND ACCURACY

Total Words Read: _____

Number of Errors: _____

Number of Correct Words
Read Per Minute (WPM):   _____

Accuracy Rate: _____

(Number of Correct Words Read per
Minute ÷ Total Words Read)

READING FLUENCY

	Low	Average	High
Decoding ability	O	O	O
Pace	O	O	O
Syntax	O	O	O
Self-correction	O	O	O
Intonation	O	O	O

Record student rates on the Oral Fluency Scores pages.

UNIT 3

Name _____ Date _____ Score _____

Narrative Writing

Writing Situation
Buying a gift for someone

Audience
People who do not know you

Directions for Writing
Think about a time you bought a gift for someone. It can be any type of gift. Explain why you bought this gift and describe how you bought it. Tell about what happened when you gave the gift.

Checklist
You will earn the best score if you
- think about what happened before you start writing.
- have a good beginning, middle, and end to your story.
- use describing words so the reader can visualize what happened.
- write paragraphs that focus on related ideas.
- use transition words to go from one idea to another.
- tell about the characters in your story, including yourself.
- tell events in the order they happen.
- use subjects, verbs, and modifiers correctly.
- write more sentences and longer sentences when you revise.
- use words that tell how you felt about buying and giving the gift.

Four Point Rubrics for Narrative Writing

Genre	1 Point	2 Points	3 Points	4 Points
Narrative	Narrative has missing details or elements. Logical order and narrative structure is unclear. Plot does not include a viable problem. Character development is not apparent. Setting does not include descriptions of where and when the narrative is set.	Narrative includes plot outline and some descriptive details and elements that add excitement or color, but narrative structure is not entirely clear. Character development is minimal. Setting includes minimal descriptions of where and when the narrative is set.	Narrative includes fairly well developed plot with descriptive details and other elements such as subplots that are integrated into the resolution. Narrative structure is clear. Characters are developed, though some characters may seem superficial. Setting includes descriptions of where and when the narrative is set.	Narrative includes more complicated plot lines with varied timelines, flashbacks, or dual story lines. Narrative structure is well defined. Characters well defined throughout, with unique qualities integral to the plot. Setting includes detailed descriptions of where and when the narrative is set.
Narrative: Theme	No theme is apparent.	Superficial theme is included but not integrated.	A theme is expressed but not well developed.	The narrative fully develops a theme that expresses an underlying message beyond the narrative plot.
Writing Traits				
Audience	Displays little or no sense of audience. Does not engage audience.	Displays some sense of audience.	Writes with audience in mind throughout.	Displays a strong sense of audience. Engages audience.
Voice	The writing provides little sense of involvement or commitment. There is no evidence that the writer has chosen a suitable voice.	The writer's commitment to the topic seems inconsistent. A sense of the writer may emerge at times; however, the voice is either inappropriately personal or inappropriately impersonal.	A voice is present. The writer demonstrates commitment to the topic. In places, the writing is expressive, engaging, or sincere. Words and expressions are clear and precise.	The writer has chosen a voice appropriate for the topic, purpose, and audience. Unique style comes through. The writing is expressive, engaging, or sincere. Strong commitment to the topic.
Writing Conventions				
Conventions Overall	Numerous errors in usage, grammar, spelling, capitalization, and punctuation repeatedly distract the reader and make the text difficult to read. The reader finds it difficult to focus on the message.	The writing demonstrates limited control of standard writing conventions (punctuation, spelling, capitalization, grammar, and usage). Errors sometimes impede readability.	The writing demonstrates control of standard writing conventions (punctuation, spelling, capitalization, grammar, and usage). Minor errors, while perhaps noticeable, do not impede readability.	The writing demonstrates exceptionally strong control of standard writing conventions (punctuation, spelling, capitalization, grammar, and usage) and uses them effectively to enhance communication. Errors are so few and so minor that the reader can easily skim over them.

Six Point Rubrics

Use the following rubrics to assess student writing.

6 Points

The writing is focused, purposeful, and reflects insight into the writing situation. The paper conveys a sense of completeness and wholeness with adherence to the main idea, and its organizational pattern provides for a logical progression of ideas. The support is substantial, specific, relevant, concrete, and/or illustrative. The paper demonstrates a commitment to and an involvement with the subject, clarity in presentation of ideas, and may use creative writing strategies appropriate to the purpose of the paper. The writing demonstrates a mature command of language (word choice) with freshness of expression. Sentence structure is varied, and sentences are complete except when fragments are used purposefully. Few, if any, convention errors occur in mechanics, usage, and punctuation.

5 Points

The writing focuses on the topic, and its organizational pattern provides for a progression of ideas, although some lapses may occur. The paper conveys a sense of completeness or wholeness. The support is ample. The writing demonstrates a mature command of language, including precise word choice. There is variation in sentence structure, and, with rare exceptions, sentences are complete except when fragments are used purposefully. The paper generally follows the conventions of mechanics, usage, and spelling.

4 Points

The writing is generally focused on the topic but may include extraneous or loosely related material. An organizational pattern is apparent, although some lapses may occur. The paper exhibits some sense of completeness or wholeness. The support, including word choice, is adequate, although development may be uneven. There is little variation in sentence structure, and most sentences are complete. The paper generally follows the conventions of mechanics, usage, and spelling.

3 Points

The writing is generally focused on the topic but may include extraneous or loosely related material. An organizational pattern has been attempted, but the paper may lack a sense of completeness or wholeness. Some support is included, but development is erratic. Word choice is adequate but may be limited, predictable, or occasionally vague. There is little, if any, variation in sentence structure. Knowledge of the conventions of mechanics and usage is usually demonstrated, and commonly used words are usually spelled correctly.

2 Points

The writing is related to the topic but includes extraneous or loosely related material. Little evidence of an organizational pattern may be demonstrated, and the paper may lack a sense of completeness or wholeness. Development of support is inadequate or illogical. Word choice is limited, inappropriate, or vague. There is little, if any, variation in sentence structure, and gross errors in sentence structure may occur. Errors in basic conventions of mechanics and usage may occur, and commonly used words may be misspelled.

1 Point

The writing may only minimally address the topic. The paper is fragmentary or an incoherent listing of related ideas or sentences or both. Little, if any, development of support or an organizational pattern or both is apparent. Limited or inappropriate word choice may obscure meaning. Gross errors in sentence structure and usage may impede communication. Frequent and blatant errors may occur in the basic conventions of mechanics and usage, and commonly used words may be misspelled.

Unscorable

The paper is unscorable because

- the response is not related to what the prompt requested the student to do.
- the response is simply a rewording of the prompt
- the response is a copy of a published work.
- the student refused to write.
- the response is illegible.
- the response is incomprehensible (words are arranged in such a way that no meaning is conveyed).
- the response contains an insufficient amount of writing to determine if the student was attempting to address the prompt.

Oral Fluency Scores

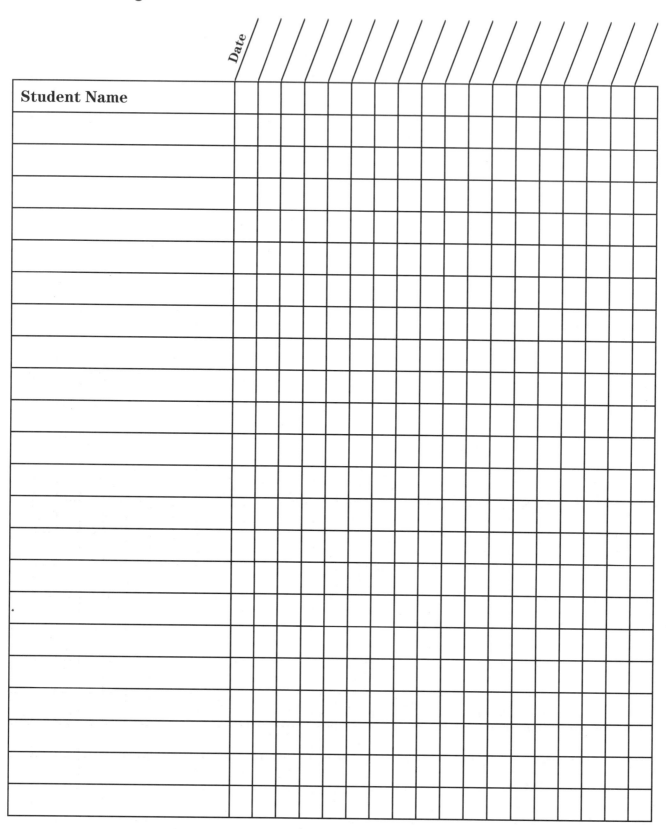

Student Name	Date															

Oral Fluency Scores

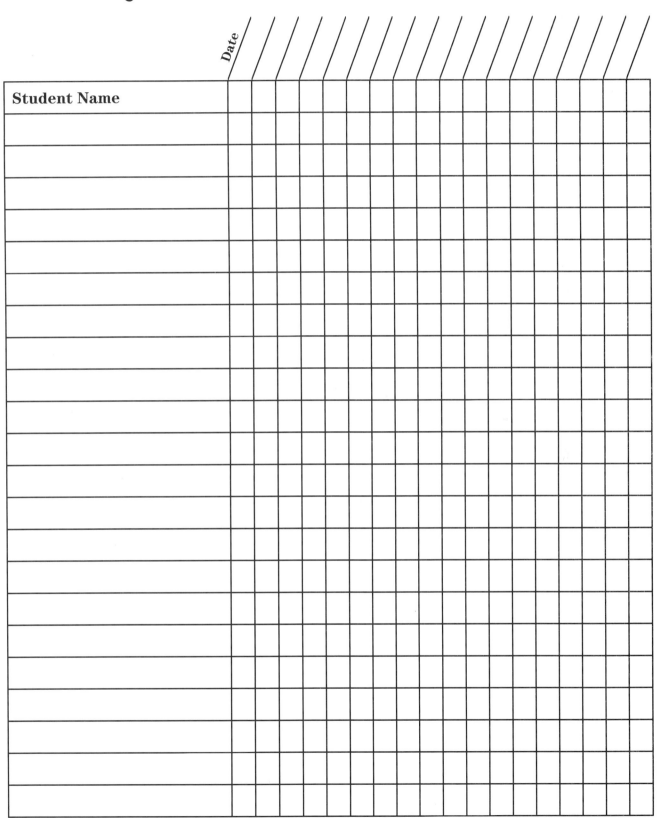

Class Assessment Record

Student Name	Unit 1, Lesson 1	Unit 1, Lesson 2	Unit 1, Lesson 3	Unit 1, Lesson 4	Unit 1, Lesson 5	Unit 1 Writing Prompt	Unit 2, Lesson 1	Unit 2, Lesson 2	Unit 2, Lesson 3

Class Assessment Record

Student Name	Unit 2, Lesson 4	Unit 2, Lesson 5	Unit 2 Writing Prompt	Unit 3, Lesson 1	Unit 3, Lesson 2	Unit 3, Lesson 3	Unit 3, Lesson 4	Unit 3, Lesson 5	Unit 3 Writing Prompt

Student Assessment Record

Name _____

Teacher _____ Grade _____

Unit/ Lesson	Assessment Section	Date	Number Possible	Number Right	%	Score (Rubrics/WPM)

Comprehension Observation Log

Student _____ **Date** _____

Unit _____ **Lesson** _____ **Selection Title** _____

General Comprehension
Concepts discussed: _____
_____

Behavior Within a Group
Articulates, expresses ideas: _____
_____

Joins discussions: _____
_____

Collaborates (such as *works well with other students, works alone*): _____
_____

Role in Group
Role (such as *leader, summarizer, questioner, critic, observer, non-participant*): _____
_____

Flexibility (changes roles when necessary): _____
_____

Use of Reading Strategies
Uses strategies when needed (either those taught or student's choice of strategy)/Describes strategies used:
_____
_____
_____

Changes strategies when appropriate: _____
_____

Changes Since Last Observation
_____
_____
_____
